SADLIER
VOCABULARY WORKSHOP®
ENRICHED EDITION

Level C

Jerome Shostak

Senior Series Consultant

Vicki A. Jacobs, Ed.D.
Associate Director, Teacher Education Program
Lecturer on Education
Harvard Graduate School of Education
Cambridge, Massachusetts

Series Consultants

Louis P. De Angelo, Ed.D.
Associate Superintendent
Diocese of Wilmington
Wilmington, Delaware

Sarah Ressler Wright, NBCT
English Department Chair
Rutherford B. Hayes High School
Delaware City Schools, Ohio

John Heath, Ph.D.
Professor of Classics
Santa Clara University
Santa Clara, California

Carolyn E. Waters, JD, Ed.S.
ELA/Literacy 6–12 Supervisor
Cobb County School District
Marietta, Georgia

S® Sadlier

Reviewers

The publisher wishes to thank for their comments and suggestions the following teachers and administrators, who read portions of the series prior to publication.

Teresa Appleby
English Teacher
Paxon Hollow Middle School
Marple Newtown District
Broomall, Pennsylvania

Laura Braun
Assistant Principal
Sawyer School
Chicago Public Schools
Chicago, Illinois

Eileen Brosnahan
Language Arts Teacher
St. Rita Catholic School
Dallas, Texas

Colleen DeGonia
Reading/Language Arts Teacher
Worth Junior High School
Worth, Illinois

Karen Berlin Ishii
Academic and Test Prep Tutor
New York, New York

Susan W. Keogh
Associate Director
Curriculum and Instruction
Lake Highland Preparatory
Orlando, Florida

Carol H. Rohrbach
Director of Curriculum and Staff
   Development
School District of Springfield
   Township
Oreland, Pennsylvania

Scott L. Smith
Teacher
Whitewater Valley Elementary
Harrison, Ohio

Patricia Stack
English Teacher
South Park School District
South Park, Pennsylvania

Sally F. Waller
English Teacher
Loyola Blakefield Middle School
Towson, Maryland

Cover: Concept/Art and Design: MK Advertising and William H. Sadlier, Inc.; Cover pencil: Shutterstock/VikaSuh.
Photo Credits: AGPix/Rolf Nussbaumer: 146 *top.* Alamy/Archive Images: 117; Everett Collection Inc/CSU Archives: 93; Fine Art Photographs: 88 *inset*; Gina Rodgers: 189; GL Archive: 103; Lebrecht Music and Arts Photo Library: 31, 75, 169; Mary Evans Picture Library: 41, 55, 59; Melanie Eldred Photography: 61 *inset bottom*; Niday Picture Library: 89 *inset right*; Photos 12: 135; Pictorial Press Ltd: 183; PRISMA ARCHIVO: 27; Superstock: 89 *inset left.* AP Images: 22 *bottom*, 185 *right*; Nati Harnik: 61 *inset top.* Art Resource, NY/The Art Archive: 13 *top left*, 108; The Kobal Collection/20th Century Fox: 79; The Kobal Collection/First National: 155; The Kobal Collection/MGM: 97, 107; The Kobal Collection/Morgan: 173; The Kobal Collection/Sovereign/Stagescreen: 145. Artville: 108–109 *background.* Corbis/Allgeller Company: 33 *bottom*; Bettmann: 12 *right*, 21, 32 *left*, 33 *top*, 37, 69; Dorothea Lange: 71; J.E. Purdy: 184 *inset*; Passage: 23 *top*; Sandy Huffaker: 60 *inset*; Underwood & Underwood: 13 *top right*; Wally McNamee: 141; ZUMA Press/Pittsburg Post-Gazette: 131. Courtesy Central Pacific Railroad Photographic History Museum, © 2013, CPRR.org: 174–175 *background.* DRK PHOTO/Sid & Shirley Rucker: 147. Getty Images/Archive Photos/MPI: 174 *inset*; REUTERS/Seth Wenig: 164 *top*; Getty Images News/Johannes Simon: 165 *top*; Hulton Archive/Tom Munnecke: 164 *bottom*; McClatchy-Tribune/Raleigh News & Observer: 136 *inset*; Roll Call: 17; Science Faction/Jason Isley-Scubazoo: 98 *top*; Time & Life Pictures: 13 *bottom*; Time & Life Pictures/Gordon Parks: 193. The Granger Collection, New York: 32 *right*, 109 *left*, 109 *inset*, 175, 185 *left*, 185 *inset.* The Image Works/ArenaPal/Nigel Norrington: 151; Mary Evans Picture Library: 179; Roger-Viollet: 113; Syracuse Newspapers/ Chrissie Cowan: 65. Library of Congress/Prints & Photographs Division, FSA/OWI Collection, LC-USF34-016191-C/Dorothea Lange: 70 *bottom*; Prints & Photographs Division, FSA/OWI Collection, LC-USF34-016819-C/ Dorothea Lange: 70 *top.* Photo Reseachers, Inc./Gregory G. Dimijan: 146–147 *background.* Photo Researchers, Inc./Alexis Rosenfeld: 98 *bottom*; Peter Menzel: 99 *left.* Photodisc: 88 *frame*, 89 *frame*, 98–99 *background*, 109 *frame*, 109 *top*, 184 *frame.* PhotoEdit Inc./Paul Conklin: 137 *top.* Science Photo Library/David Vaughn: 99 *right.* Shutterstock/Africa Studio: 89 *center*; amasterphotographer: 60 *left*; Andrey Kekylyaynen: 60 *right*; Bakalusha: 108 banner; koya979: 137 clip; LANBO: 164–165 *background*; Mazzzur: 70 *background*, 71 *background*; Mihaela Stejskalova: 12 *left*, 13 *background*; Oleksii Sagitov: 88 *left*; Peshkova: 23 *bottom*; Picsfive: 185 *background*; Pongohan.R: 136 *background*; rangizzz: 174 *frame*, 175 *frame*; s_oleg: 88 *right*; Sailorr: 109 *background*; shivanetua: 61 *top*; sommthink: 61 *bottom*; Subbotina Anna: 22 *top*, 23 *background.* Stockbyte: 88–89 *background.* SuperStock/Ambient Images Inc.: 137 *bottom.* U.S. National Archives: 146 *bottom.* Wikipedia: 165 *bottom.*

Illustration Credits: Tim Haggerty: 46, 84, 122, 160, 198. Tristan Elwell/Shannon Associates LLC: 126–127. Zina Saunders: 50–51

S® and **VOCABULARY WORKSHOP**®
are registered trademarks of
William H. Sadlier, Inc.

Printed in the United States of America.
ISBN: 978-0-8215-8008-0
8 9 10 11 EB 21 20 19 18 17

For additional online resources, go to vocabularyworkshop.com and enter the Student Access Code: VW13SCJB52SXK

ENRICHED EDITION: New Features

For more than five decades, VOCABULARY WORKSHOP has proven to be a highly successful tool for guiding systematic vocabulary growth and developing vocabulary skills. It has also been shown to help students prepare for standardized tests.

New in this edition are the **Reading Passages, Writing, Vocabulary in Context, and Word Study** activities. Nonfiction, high-interest passages use 15 or more of the Unit vocabulary words in context. Two writing prompts require a response to the reading and provide practice in writing for standardized tests. New Vocabulary in Context activities present words from the Unit as they are used in classic works of literature. After every three units, Word Study activities, developed in conjunction with Common Core State Standards requirements, provide practice with idioms, adages, and proverbs, as well as denotation and connotation and classical roots.

Look for the new **QR** (Quick Response) codes on the **Reading Passage** and **Vocabulary in Context** pages. QR codes can be read with a smartphone camera by downloading any free QR code application to a smartphone. Snap the code to listen to iWords and an audio of the Reading Passage for the Unit or to take an interactive quiz. With iWords you can listen to one word at a time or download all of the words in a Unit to listen to them at your convenience.

The new structure of VOCABULARY WORKSHOP is made up of 15 Units. Each Unit consists of the following sections: a **Reading Passage, Definitions, Choosing the Right Word, Synonyms and Antonyms, Completing the Sentence, Writing,** and **Vocabulary in Context**. Together, these exercises provide multiple and varied exposures to the taught words—an approach consistent with and supportive of research-based findings in vocabulary instruction.

Five **Reviews** cover Vocabulary for Comprehension and Two-Word Completions. Vocabulary for Comprehension is modeled on the reading sections of standardized tests, and as in those tests, it presents reading comprehension questions, including specific vocabulary-related ones, that are based on a reading passage.

A **Final Mastery Test** assesses a selection of words from the year with activities on Synonyms, Antonyms, Analogies, Two-Word Completions, Supplying Words in Context, Word Associations, and Choosing the Right Meaning.

In each level of VOCABULARY WORKSHOP, 300 key words are taught. The words have been selected according to the following criteria: currency and general usefulness; frequency of appearance on recognized vocabulary lists; applicability to, and appearance on, standardized tests; and current grade-level research.

ONLINE COMPONENTS
vocabularyworkshop.com

At **vocabularyworkshop.com** you will find iWords, an audio program that provides pronunciations, definitions, and examples of usage for all of the key words presented in this level of VOCABULARY WORKSHOP. You can listen to one word at a time or download all of the words of any given Unit. You will then be able to listen to the audio program for that Unit at your convenience.

At **vocabularyworkshop.com** you will also find **Audio Passages, interactive vocabulary quizzes, flashcards, games and puzzles** that will help reinforce and enrich your understanding of the key words in this level of VOCABULARY WORKSHOP.

CONTENTS

ENRICHED EDITION: New Features .... *iii*

VOCABULARY STRATEGY: Using Context 7

VOCABULARY STRATEGY: Word Structure 8

VOCABULARY AND READING 9

WORKING WITH ANALOGIES 11

UNIT 1 Vocabulary: adage, bonanza, churlish, citadel, collaborate, decree, discordant, evolve, excerpt, grope, hover, jostle, laggard, plaudits, preclude, revert, rubble, servile, vigil, wrangle
   Passage: **Greetings from the WPA** \<Letters\> *12*
   Definitions and Exercises *14–20*
   Vocabulary in Context: Literary Text (Baroness Orczy) *21*

UNIT 2 Vocabulary: antics, avowed, banter, bountiful, congested, detriment, durable, enterprising, frugal, gingerly, glut, incognito, invalidate, legendary, maim, minimize, oblique, veer, venerate, wanton
   Passage: **Instant Cash!** \<Expository Essay\> *22*
   Definitions and Exercises *24–30*
   Vocabulary in Context: Literary Text (O. Henry) *31*

UNIT 3 Vocabulary: allot, amass, audacious, comply, devoid, elite, grapple, incapacitate, instigate, longevity, myriad, perspective, perturb, prodigious, relevant, skittish, tether, unison, vie, willful
   Passage: **Grand Columbian Carnival Unites the World** \<Press Release\> *32*
   Definitions and Exercises *34–40*
   Vocabulary in Context: Literary Text (Henry David Thoreau) *41*

REVIEW UNITS 1–3
   Vocabulary for Comprehension *42*
   Two-Word Completions *44*

WORD STUDY
   Idioms *45*
   Denotation and Connotation *47*
   Classical Roots *49*

UNIT 4 Vocabulary: annul, blasé, bolster, deplore, frivolous, muster, nonentity, obsess, ornate, oust, peruse, porous, promontory, prone, qualm, recourse, residue, solicitous, staid, sustain
   Passage: **Toni Cade Bambara** \<Author Profile\> *50*
   Definitions and Exercises *52–58*
   Vocabulary in Context: Literary Text (Edgar Allan Poe) *59*

UNIT 5 Vocabulary: addendum, aghast, ample, apparition, assert, cower, disdain, epitaph, ethical, facetious, inaudible, indiscriminate, intrigue, jurisdiction, plausible, plebeian, prodigal, proximity, pulverize, volatile
   Passage: **Reality Check** \<Persuasive Essay\> *60*
   Definitions and Exercises *62–68*
   Vocabulary in Context: Literary Text (Charles Dickens) *69*

UNIT 6 Vocabulary: abashed, aloof, anguish, articulate, bask, defect, finesse, flaunt, forthright, genial, instill, ostracize, premonition, pseudonym, purge, rehabilitate, repercussion, resolute, retentive, scapegoat
   Passage: **Diary of a Young Migrant Worker** \<Diary Entry\> *70*

Definitions and Exercises *72–78*
Vocabulary in Context: Literary Text (Jack London) *79*

REVIEW UNITS 4–6
Vocabulary for Comprehension *80*
Two-Word Completions *82*

WORD STUDY
Idioms *83*
Denotation and Connotation *85*
Classical Roots *87*

UNIT 7 Vocabulary: acme, attribute, belittle, convey, doctrine, excise, exotic, haggard, jaunty, juncture, menial, parry, predatory, ravage, stance, tawdry, turncoat, unassuming, wallow, waver
Passage: **The Discriminating Pigeon** <Magazine Article> *88*
Definitions and Exercises *90–96*
Vocabulary in Context: Literary Text (Louisa May Alcott) *97*

UNIT 8 Vocabulary: abut, attire, avail, crony, cryptic, divergent, enmity, fervent, gaunt, infiltrate, nullify, perceptible, plummet, proclaim, proxy, rankle, scavenger, stint, stoical, unflagging
Passage: **Aquatic Robotics** <Technical Essay> *98*
Definitions and Exercises *100–106*
Vocabulary in Context: Literary Text (Stephen Crane) *107*

UNIT 9 Vocabulary: apt, awry, bludgeon, capitulate, chafe, defile, dire, disarming, disgruntled, encroach, endow, fend, impunity, mien, penal, pertinent, predominant, prodigy, recluse, renown
Passage: **Tecumseh of the Shawnee** <Biographical Sketch> *108*
Definitions and Exercises *110–116*
Vocabulary in Context: Literary Text (Mark Twain) *117*

REVIEW UNITS 7–9
Vocabulary for Comprehension *118*
Two-Word Completions *120*

WORD STUDY
Proverbs *121*
Denotation and Connotation *123*
Classical Roots *125*

UNIT 10 Vocabulary: accord, barter, curt, devise, dexterous, engross, entail, ferret, habituate, impending, personable, rue, scoff, transition, trepidation, upbraid, veritable, vex, vitality, whimsical
Passage: **The Adventures of Narváez and Cabeza de Vaca in the New World**
<Historical Nonfiction> *126*
Definitions and Exercises *128–134*
Vocabulary in Context: Literary Text (Edgar Rice Burroughs) *135*

UNIT 11 Vocabulary: appease, belated, calamitous, cite, conventional, decoy, delve, ensue, gallantry, impart, judicious, mediate, milieu, outlandish, overbearing, pert, quirk, regale, shiftless, taint
Passage: **Working Like a Dog** <Interview> *136*
Definitions and Exercises *138–144*
Vocabulary in Context: Literary Text (E.M. Forster) *145*

UNIT 12 Vocabulary: abdicate, bestow, capacious, caustic, crusade, deface, embargo, fallacy, levity, mendicant, nauseate, negate, pivotal, recipient, ruse, teem, tenet, tractable, ungainly, voracious

    Passage: To The Bat Cave! <Informational Essay> 146

    Definitions and Exercises *148–154*

    Vocabulary in Context: Literary Text (Sir Arthur Conan Doyle)......................... 155

REVIEW UNITS 10–12

    Vocabulary for Comprehension *156*

    Two-Word Completions *158*

WORD STUDY

    Idioms *159*

    Denotation and Connotation *161*

    Classical Roots *163*

UNIT 13 Vocabulary: adapt, attest, dovetail, enormity, falter, foreboding, forlorn, haughty, impediment, imperative, loiter, malinger, pithy, plunder, simper, steadfast, vaunted, vilify, waif, wry

    Passage: Steven P. Jobs: 1955–2011 <Obituary>.............................*164*

    Definitions and Exercises *166–172*

    Vocabulary in Context: Literary Text (George Eliot).............................*173*

UNIT 14 Vocabulary: amplify, armistice, arrogant, bland, disclaim, epoch, estrange, gratify, infinite, irascible, kindred, naive, niche, obliterate, ramshackle, ransack, rote, solvent, tedious, vendor

    Passage: Now Arriving on Track 1: New York Dry Goods <Letter> *174*

    Definitions and Exercises *176–182*

    Vocabulary in Context: Literary Text (Robert Louis Stevenson).........................*183*

UNIT 15 Vocabulary: abyss, befall, crucial, dregs, embody, exasperate, fiasco, garnish, heritage, inert, mercenary, negligent, oblivion, opus, pallid, parable, rational, reciprocal, stricture, veneer

    Passage: Muckraking Journalist Ida M. Tarbell <Biographical Sketch> *184*

    Definitions and Exercises *186–192*

    Vocabulary in Context: Literary Text (Henry James).......................................*193*

REVIEW UNITS 13–15

    Vocabulary for Comprehension *194*

    Two-Word Completions *196*

WORD STUDY

    Adages *197*

    Denotation and Connotation *199*

    Classical Roots *201*

FINAL MASTERY TEST..*202*

INDEX..*207*

iWords Audio Program available at **vocabularyworkshop.com**.

VOCABULARY STRATEGY: Using Context

The **context** of a word is the printed text of which that word is part. By studying the word's context, we may find **clues** to its meaning. We might find a clue in the immediate or adjoining sentence or phrase in which the word appears; in the topic or subject matter of the passage; or in the physical features—such as photographs, illustrations, charts, graphs, captions and headings—of a page itself.

The **Vocabulary in Context**, **Vocabulary for Comprehension**, and **Choosing the Right Meaning** exercises that appear in the Units, the Reviews, and Final Mastery Test provide practice in using context to decode unfamiliar words.

Three types of context clues appear in the exercises in this book.

A **restatement clue** consists of a *synonym* for or a *definition* of the missing word. For example:

The _____, overbearing king refused to hear the poor workman's plea.

a. arrogant   **b.** disarming   **c.** fervent   **d.** legendary

In this sentence, *overbearing* is a synonym of the missing word, *arrogant*, and acts as a restatement clue for it.

A **contrast clue** consists of an *antonym* for or a phrase that means the opposite of the missing word. For example:

"It seems to me that the coach is even-tempered," I said,

"But many of my teammates find the coach (**irascible, porous**)."

In this sentence, *even-tempered* is an antonym of the missing word, *irascible*. This is confirmed by the presence of the word *but*, which indicates that the answer must be the opposite of *even-tempered*.

An **inference clue** implies but does not directly state the meaning of the missing word or words. For example:

The _____ patient had lost a lot of weight in a short period of time, but his energy was _____ and he kept up his usual busy schedule.

a. abashed . . . calamitous   **c.** resolute . . . whimsical
b. judicious . . . bountiful   **d.** gaunt . . . unflagging

In this sentence, there are several inference clues: (a) the phrase *had lost a lot of weight* suggests *gaunt*; (b) the words *kept up his usual busy schedule* suggest the word *unflagging*. These words are inference clues because they suggest or imply, but do not directly state, the missing word or words.

VOCABULARY STRATEGY: Word Structure

Prefixes, **suffixes**, and **roots**, or **bases**, are word parts. One strategy for determining an unknown word's meaning is to "take apart" the word and think about the parts. Study the prefixes and suffixes below to help you find out the meanings of words in which they appear.

Prefix	Meaning	Sample Words
com-, con-	together, with	compatriot, contact
de-, dis-, di-	down, away from, not	devalue, disloyal, dichromatic
il-, im-, in-, ir, non-, un-	apart, opposite not	illegal, impossible, inactive, irregular, nonsense, unable
sub-, sup- super-	under, less than above, greater than	submarine, support superimpose, superstar

Noun Suffix	Meaning	Sample Nouns
-acy, -ance, -ence, -hood, -ity, -ment, -ness, -ship	state, quality, or condition of, act or process of	adequacy, attendance, persistence, neighborhood, activity, judgment, brightness, friendship
-ant, -eer, -ent, -er, -ian, -ier, -ist, -or	one who does or makes something	auctioneer, contestant, resident, banker, comedian, financier, dentist, doctor
-ation, -ition, -ion	act or result of	organization, imposition, election

Verb Suffix	Meaning	Sample Verbs
-ate	to become, produce, or treat	validate, salivate, chlorinate
-efy, -ify, -ize	to cause, make	liquefy, glorify, legalize

Adjective Suffix	Meaning	Sample Adjectives
-able, -ible	able, capable of relating	believable, incredible
-al, -ic	to, characteristic of full of,	natural, romantic
-ful, -ive, -ous	given to, marked by like,	beautiful, protective, poisonous
-ish, -like	resembling	foolish, childlike
-less	lacking, without	careless

A **base** or **root** is the main part of a word to which prefixes and suffixes may be added. On the Classical Roots page of the Word Study section, you will learn more about Latin and Greek roots and the English words that derive from them. The following lists may help you figure out the meaning of new or unfamiliar words.

Greek Root	Meaning	Sample Words
-cryph-, -crypt-	hidden, secret	apocryphal, cryptographer
-dem-, -demo-	people	epidemic, democracy
-gen-	race, kind, origin, birth	generation
-gnos-	know	diagnostic
-lys-, -lyt-	break down	analysis, electrolyte, catalytic

Latin Root	Meaning	Sample Words
-cap-, -capt-, -cept-, -cip-	take	captive, concept, recipient
-cede-, -ceed-, -ceas- -cess-	happen, yield, go	precede, proceed, decease, cessation
-fac-, -fact-, -fect-, -fic-	make	faculty, artifact, defect, beneficial
-tac-, -tag-, -tang-, -teg-	touch	contact, contagious, tangible, integral
-tain-, -ten-, -tin-	hold, keep	contain, tenure, retinue

For more prefixes, suffixes, and roots, visit **vocabularyworkshop.com**.

VOCABULARY AND READING

Word knowledge is essential to reading comprehension. Your knowledge of word meanings and ability to think carefully about what you read will help you succeed in school and on standardized tests, including the SAT, the ACT, and the PSAT.

New **Reading Passages** provide extra practice with vocabulary words. Vocabulary words are boldfaced to draw your attention to their uses and contexts. Context clues embedded in the passages encourage you to figure out the meanings of words before you read the definitions provided on the pages directly following the passages.

You will read excerpts from classic literature in the **Vocabulary in Context** exercises. Each excerpt includes one of the Unit vocabulary words as it is used in the original work. You may use what you learn about the word from its use in context to answer questions on the definition.

The **Vocabulary for Comprehension** exercises in each review consist of a nonfiction reading passage followed by comprehension questions. The passages and questions are similar to those that you are likely to find on standardized tests.

Kinds of Questions

Main Idea Questions generally ask what the passage as a whole is about. Often, but not always, the main idea is stated in the first paragraph of the passage. You may also be asked the main idea of a specific paragraph. Questions about the main idea may begin like this:

- The primary or main purpose of the passage is . . .
- The passage is best described as . . .
- The title that best describes the content of the passage is . . .

Detail Questions focus on important information that is explicitly stated in the passage. Often, however, the correct answer choices do not use the exact language of the passage. They are instead restatements, or paraphrases, of the text.

Vocabulary-in-Context Questions check your ability to use context to identify a word's meaning. Use line references to see how and in what context the word is used. For example:

- **Exotic** (line 8) is best defined as . . .
- The meaning of **turncoat** (line 30) is . . .

Use context to check your answer choices, particularly when the vocabulary word has more than one meaning. Among the choices may be two (or more) correct meanings of the word in question. Choose the meaning that best fits the context.

Inference Questions ask you to make inferences or draw conclusions from the passage. These questions often begin like this:

- It can be inferred from the passage that . . .
- The author implies that . . .
- Evidently the author feels that . . .

The inferences you make and the conclusions you draw must be based on the information in the passage. Your own knowledge and reasoning come into play in understanding what is implied and in reaching conclusions that are logical.

Questions About Tone show your understanding of the author's attitude toward the subject of the passage. Words that describe tone, or attitude, are "feeling" words, such as *bored, unsure, scornful, amazed, respectful*. These are typical questions:

- The author's attitude toward . . . is best described as . . .
- Which word best describes the author's tone?

To determine the tone, pay attention to the author's word choice. The author's attitude may be positive (respectful), negative (scornful), or neutral (distant).

Questions About Author's Technique focus on the way a text is organized and the language the author uses. These questions ask you to think about structure and function. For example:

- The final paragraph serves to . . .
- The author cites . . . in order to . . .

To answer the questions, you must demonstrate an understanding of the way the author presents information and develops ideas.

Strategies

Here are some general strategies to help you as you read each passage and answer the questions.

- Read the introduction first if there is one. The introduction will provide a focus for the passage.

- Be an active reader. As you read, ask yourself questions about the passage—for example: What is this paragraph about? What does the writer mean here? Why does the writer include this information?

- Refer to the passage when you answer the questions. In general, the order of the questions mirrors the organization of the passage, and many of the questions include paragraph or line references. It is often helpful to go back and reread before choosing an answer.

- Read carefully, and be sure to base your answer choices on the passage. There are answer choices that make sense but are not based on the information in the passage. These are true statements, but they are incorrect answers. The correct answers are either restatements of ideas in the text or inferences that can be drawn from the text.

- Consider each exercise a learning experience. Keep in mind that your ability to answer the questions correctly shows as much about your understanding of the questions as about your understanding of the passage.

WORKING WITH ANALOGIES

A verbal analogy expresses a relationship or comparison between sets of words. Normally, an analogy contains two pairs of words linked by a word or symbol that stands for an equal (=) sign. A complete analogy compares the two pairs of words and makes a statement about them. It asserts that the relationship between the first—or key—pair of words is the same as the relationship between the second pair.

In the **Analogies** exercises in the Final Mastery Test, you will be asked to complete analogies—that is, to choose the pair of words that best matches or parallels the relationship of the key, or given, pair of words. Here are two examples:

1. **maple** is to **tree** as
   a. acorn is to oak
   b. hen is to rooster
   c. rose is to flower
   d. shrub is to lilac

2. **joyful** is to **gloomy** as
   a. cheerful is to happy
   b. strong is to weak
   c. quick is to famous
   d. hungry is to starving

In order to find the correct answer to exercise 1, you must first determine the relationship between the two key words, **maple** and **tree**. In this case, that relationship might be expressed as "a maple is a kind (or type) of tree." The next step is to select from choices a, b, c, and d the pair of words that best reflects the same relationship. The correct answer is c; it is the only pair whose relationship parallels the one in the key words: A rose is a kind (or type) of flower, just as a maple is a kind (or type) of tree. The other choices do not express the same relationship.

In exercise 2, the relationship between the key words can be expressed as "joyful means the opposite of gloomy." Which of the choices best represents the same relationship? The answer is b: "strong means the opposite of weak."

Here are examples of some other common analogy relationships:

Analogy	Key Relationship
big is to **large** as **little** is to **small**	**Big** means the same thing as **large**, just as **little** means the same thing as **small**.
brave is to **favorable** as **cowardly** is to **unfavorable**	The tone of **brave** is **favorable**, just as the tone of **cowardly** is **unfavorable**.
busybody is to **nosy** as **klutz** is to **clumsy**	A **busybody** is by definition someone who is **nosy**, just as a **klutz** is by definition someone who is **clumsy**.
cowardly is to **courage** as **awkward** is to **grace**	Someone who is **cowardly** lacks **courage**, just as someone who is **awkward** lacks **grace**.
visible is to **see** as **audible** is to **hear**	If something is **visible**, you can by definition **see** it, just as if something is **audible**, you can by definition **hear** it.
liar is to **truthful** as **bigot** is to **fair-minded**	A **liar** is by definition not likely to be **truthful**, just as a **bigot** is by definition not likely to be **fair-minded**.
eyes are to **see** as **ears** are to **hear**	You use your **eyes** to **see** with, just as you use your **ears** to **hear** with.

There are many different kinds of relationships represented in the analogy questions you will find in the Final Mastery Test, but the key to solving any analogy is to find and express the relationship between the two key words.

Read the following passage, taking note of the **boldface** words and their contexts. These words are among those you will be studying in Unit 1. As you complete the exercises in this Unit, it may help to refer to the way the words are used below.

Greetings from the WPA
<Letters>

Twenty-five percent of workers in the United States were unemployed during the height of the Great Depression. President Franklin Delano Roosevelt's administration created the Works Progress Administration (WPA). It employed over eight million people in construction and arts projects from 1935 to 1943.

April 10, 1937
Butte, Montana

Dearest Rose,

I'd say I've been meaning to write for ages and I think of you often, but I know you loathe that sort of **servile** sentimentality, and I wouldn't want to **wrangle** about it next time we meet. Moe and I were just talking about when the three of us were together in Chicago. We got to reminiscing, and soon we were goofing around like we used to—we must have **reverted** halfway to infancy! He said you're working for the Works Progress Administration in New York. I've been writing for the WPA myself.

Things got worse in Chicago after you left. I was in and out of odd jobs, mostly out of them, and I moved back to Montana. I stayed in Missoula for a bit, at my parents' house, which is the same **citadel** of good manners and polite conversation that I remember. I'm grateful they took me in, but I felt uncomfortable about it. I don't know why I should feel like a **laggard** when everyone else is out of work, too, but it really got me down and put me in a **churlish** state of mind. After weeks of grumpily **hovering** around the house, I found work at a ranch that provided room and board.

When that job ended, I lucked into some work for the WPA. I'm writing "objective descriptions" of town, countryside, and work projects. I watched construction on the Fort Peck Dam. Now I'm in Butte, climbing through **rubble** and machinery at the copper mines nearby. By official **decree**, I'm here to record facts and figures, but I can't resist interviewing the miners, and I believe this is the best writing work I've done. I'll send you an **excerpt** once I've written more.

Send a letter if you can, or maybe I'll come see you in New York when I'm done with Butte.

Yours,
Henry

FRANKLIN D.
ROOSEVELT

Teletype operators in the federal office of the WPA, 1937

WPA artists at work on a mural;
Woman displaying WPA poster, 1936

June 3, 1937
New York City, New York

Dear Henry,

It's been hard times out east, too, and worse this year, just after it had seemed the country was **groping** its way back to normalcy. The only artists I know making a living with their art are working for the WPA, and I'm lucky to be one of them. I've done a series of woodcuts for posters and may soon have a chance to **collaborate** with another painter on a mural for a hospital. Some of the work that the WPA artists produce is very good, but I haven't spent as much time worrying about **plaudits** and praise as about keeping the work lined up. Around two thousand New York artists are working for the Federal Arts Project this year. The pay's not much, but I wonder what I'd be doing without it. Wonder is the beginning of wisdom, but that's a kind of wisdom I'm happy to put off.

Just back from waiting on the predictably long line for our paychecks. It's become a social event. We pass the time chatting about painting and **jostling** each other out of line for a laugh.

I can hardly imagine you in New York, but that doesn't **preclude** your arrival.

Love,
Rose

Relief workers on a cable during the construction of the Fort Peck Dam, 1936

Audio

For iWords and audio passages, snap the code, or go to **vocabularyworkshop.com**.

Definitions

Note the spelling, pronunciation, part(s) of speech, and definition(s) of each of the following words. Then write the appropriate form of the word in the blank spaces in the illustrative sentence(s) following. Finally, study the lists of synonyms and antonyms.

1. adage
(ad' ij)

(*n.*) a proverb, wise saying

One way to begin an informal speech or an oral report is to quote an old _____.

SYNONYMS: maxim, aphorism

2. bonanza
(bə nan' zə)

(*n.*) a rich mass of ore in a mine; something very valuable, profitable, or rewarding; a source of wealth or prosperity; a very large amount; sudden profit or gain

The thrilling adventure movie set in Alaska proved to be a box-office _____.

SYNONYM: windfall

3. churlish
(chər' lish)

(*adj.*) lacking politeness or good manners; lacking sensitivity; difficult to work with or deal with; rude

The store manager instructed all the salesclerks to avoid _____ replies to customers' questions.

SYNONYMS: surly, ill-tempered
ANTONYMS: courteous, civil, well-mannered

4. citadel
(sit' ə del)

(*n.*) a fortress that overlooks and protects a city; any strong or commanding place

A medieval _____ once guarded the capital city of the Greek island of Rhodes.

SYNONYMS: fort, stronghold, bulwark, bastion

5. collaborate
(kə lab' ə rāt)

(*v.*) to work with, work together

Several students plan to _____ on a geology project for the annual science fair.

SYNONYMS: team up, join forces
ANTONYM: work alone

6. decree
(di krē')

(*n.*) an order having the force of law; (*v.*) to issue such an order; to command firmly or forcefully

Caesar Augustus issued a _____ that all the world be taxed.

Why does nature always seem to _____ nasty weather for our annual family picnic?

SYNONYMS: (*n.*) proclamation, edict; (*v.*) proclaim

7. discordant
(dis kôr' dənt)

(adj.) disagreeable in sound, jarring; lacking in harmony

Their little spat struck a _____ note in our otherwise happy family get-together.

SYNONYMS: grating, shrill, different, divergent, conflicting
ANTONYMS: harmonious, in agreement

8. evolve
(ē välv')

(v.) to develop gradually; to rise to a higher level

Authors hope that their notes, descriptions, and character sketches will _____ into a book.

SYNONYMS: unfold, emerge; ANTONYMS: wither, atrophy

9. excerpt
(ek' sərpt)

(n.) a passage taken from a book, article, etc.; (v.) to take such a passage; to quote

My essay includes a long _____ from a speech by Sojourner Truth.

If you _____ some material from a reference book, be sure to enclose it in quotation marks.

SYNONYMS: (n.) portion, section, extract

10. grope
(grōp)

(v.) to feel about hesitantly with the hands; to search blindly and uncertainly

When the power failed, we had to _____ in the dark to find a working flashlight.

SYNONYMS: fumble for, cast about for

11. hover
(həv' ər)

(v.) to float or hang suspended over; to move back and forth uncertainly over or around

A large group of vultures _____ in the air above the wounded animal.

SYNONYMS: linger, waver, seesaw; ANTONYM: soar

12. jostle
(jäs' əl)

(v.) to make or force one's way by pushing or elbowing; to bump, brush against; to compete for

I tried not to _____ other riders as I exited the crowded bus.

SYNONYM: push

13. laggard
(lag' ərd)

(n.) a person who moves slowly or falls behind; (adj.) falling behind; slow to move, act, or respond

Tour guides often have to urge _____ to keep up with the rest of the group.

Tenants who are _____ in paying rent run the risk of being forced to move.

SYNONYMS: (n.) slowpoke, straggler; (adj.) sluggish
ANTONYMS: (n.) early bird; (adj.) swift, speedy, prompt

14. plaudits
(plô′ ditz)

(*n., pl.*) applause; enthusiastic praise or approval

The skaters who won the gold medals gratefully accepted the _____ of their fans.

SYNONYMS: cheers, acclaim
ANTONYMS: boos, disapproval, ridicule

15. preclude
(prē klüd′)

(*v.*) to make impossible, prevent, shut out

Three wrong answers will _____ any contestant from entering the quiz show's final round.

SYNONYMS: hinder, check, stop
ANTONYMS: help, promote, facilitate

16. revert
(rē vərt′)

(*v.*) to return, go back

Control of a property usually _____ to the legal owner when a lease is up.

SYNONYMS: relapse, regress
ANTONYMS: progress, advance

17. rubble
(rəb′ əl)

(*n.*) broken stone or bricks; ruins

Bulldozers and wrecking balls soon reduced the damaged building to a heap of smoking _____.

SYNONYM: wreckage

18. servile
(sər′ vīl)

(*adj.*) of or relating to a slave; behaving like or suitable for a slave or a servant, menial; lacking spirit or independence, abjectly submissive

Most serious performers prefer constructive criticism to _____ flattery.

SYNONYMS: slavish, groveling
ANTONYMS: masterly, overbearing

19. vigil
(vij′ əl)

(*n.*) a watch, especially at night; any period of watchful attention

Thousands attended the solemn _____ at the Vietnam Veterans Memorial.

20. wrangle
(raŋ′ gəl)

(*v.*) to quarrel or argue in a noisy, angry way; to obtain by argument; to herd; (*n.*) a noisy quarrel

My brother and sister always _____ over whose turn it is to take out the trash.

The customer got into a nasty _____ with the shopkeeper.

SYNONYMS: (*v.*) squabble, bicker
ANTONYMS: (*v.*) agree, concur

Choosing the Right Word

Select the **boldface** word that better completes each sentence. You might refer to the passage on pages 12–13 to see how most of these words are used in context.

1. Under the Articles of Confederation, the thirteen states (**hovered, wrangled**) so much that the nation seemed to be in danger of breaking up.

2. All those who (**decreed, collaborated**) with the enemy in the hope of gaining special favors will be punished severely.

3. The little club that they set up to talk over community problems (**evolved, jostled**) over the years into a national political organization.

4. As we searched through the (**rubble, citadel**) after the earthquake, it was heartbreaking to find such articles as a teakettle and a child's doll.

5. Every time he quotes an old (**vigil, adage**), he looks as though he has just had a brilliant new idea.

6. She raised so many objections to attending the dance that it was obvious she was (**groping, precluding**) for an excuse not to go.

John Hanson, President of the Continental Congress, governed the American colonies under the Articles of Confederation.

7. The "broken down old furniture" that the woman left to her children turned out to be a (**bonanza, rubble**) of valuable antiques.

8. I chose to read a(n) (**decree, excerpt**) from *Leaves of Grass* by Walt Whitman for my poetry recitation.

9. The assembly speaker may have been boring, but that was no excuse for the students' (**laggard, churlish**) behavior toward him.

10. At midnight, the sentry took his post, standing (**citadel, vigil**) over the cache of weapons.

11. For weeks, an anxious world (**wrangled, hovered**) between war and peace as diplomats desperately struggled to resolve the crisis.

12. After much (**wrangling, precluding**), the student council was able to convince the principal to give students more passing time between classes.

13. A president needs advisors who will frankly explain what they really think, rather than just offer (**servile, discordant**) agreement and constant approval.

14. The landscape artists want to (**collaborate, evolve**) with the architects so that the entire house looks as though it is part of the natural environment.

15. The committee found it impossible to reach any agreement on the matter because the views of its members were so (**churlish, discordant**).

16. When I fumbled the ball on the three-yard line, the (**plaudits, excerpts**) of the crowd suddenly turned into jeers and catcalls.

17. After I had broken curfew for the third time in one week, my angry parents (**precluded, decreed**) that I was grounded for the rest of the term.

18. I refuse to accept the excuse that the pressures of a new job caused you to (**revert, grope**) to your old habit of cigarette smoking.

19. There are times when we all need to be (**jostled, reverted**) away from old, familiar ideas that may no longer be as true as they once seemed.

20. The principal was quick to approve new programs for our club but (**servile, laggard**) in providing financial support for them.

21. From the hundreds of newspaper items, the lawyer carefully (**collaborated, excerpted**) three short paragraphs that supported his case.

22. The fact that he was found guilty of a felony many years ago doesn't (**evolve, preclude**) his running for mayor.

23. I have always regarded our colleges and universities as (**citadels, plaudits**) of learning and bastions against ignorance and superstition.

24. After the operation, we sat in the hospital lounge, keeping a nightlong (**vigil, bonanza**) until we heard from the doctor.

25. I hate when people (**hover, rubble**) over me when I'm on my computer.

Synonyms

*Choose the word from this Unit that is the same or most nearly the same in meaning as the **boldface** word or expression in the phrase. Write that word on the line. Use a dictionary if necessary.*

1. as the ad campaign slowly **progressed** _____

2. tried to **prohibit** further objections to the bill _____

3. an inspiring **motto** to live by _____

4. **shoved** the table so hard that it tipped over _____

5. **scrabble** for an answer to the question _____

6. represented quite a **bonus** for the company _____

7. crushed beneath many tons of **debris** _____

8. additional practice for the **cacophonous** choir _____

9. annoyed by all that **fawning** attention _____

10. kept a **lookout** while the soldiers slept _____

Antonyms

*Choose the word from this Unit that is most nearly opposite in meaning to the **boldface** word or expression in the phrase. Write that word on the line. Use a dictionary if necessary.*

1. surprised by the **melodious** ending of the piece _____

2. not paid for his **naps** on the job _____

3. known for her use of **unwise sayings** _____

4. a theory that **shrivels** when put into practice _____

5. selling an **unprofitable investment** _____

Completing the Sentence

From the words in this Unit, choose the one that best completes each of the following sentences. Write the correct word form in the space provided.

1. The cafeteria line was so crowded that I was _____ past the desserts before I could take one.

2. After the walls of their city fell to the enemy, the inhabitants withdrew to the _____ and continued the struggle from there.

3. What is the exact wording of the _____ _____ about early birds and worm-catching?

4. The swiftest members of the herd escaped the trappers' nets, but the _____ were caught.

5. During his eleven years of "personal rule," King Charles I of England bypassed Parliament and governed the country by royal _____.

6. Our teacher gave the two of us permission to _____ _____ on our reports because we were investigating related problems.

7. If you will only show a little patience, that business investment may grow into a(n) _____ for you.

8. Your silly pride about doing everything on your own _____ your getting the help you need so badly.

9. The Emancipation Proclamation of 1863 was the first step in releasing African Americans from their _____ bonds.

10. As we discussed our coming vacation, we gradually _____ a plan for a bicycle trip through New England.

11. A single word of praise from the coach meant more to me than all the loud but thoughtless _____ of the crowd.

12. With tireless devotion, the ailing child's parents kept an anxious _____ at her bedside.

13. Suddenly the _____ voices of two quarreling people burst upon my ears and jarred me out of my daydream.

14. Before the new housing project could be built, it was necessary to tear down the old houses and remove the _____.

15. For two nights, he did his homework faithfully; then he _____ to his usual lazy ways.

16. They had such a long _____ over the use of the bicycle that their mother finally forbade either of them from using it.

17. When the lights suddenly went out, I _____ my way into the kitchen to find a candle and matches.

18. On the ground, teams of paramedics administered first aid to the victims of the accident, while police helicopters _____ overhead.

19. You hurt her feelings when you reacted to her comments in such a(n) _____ way, especially since you asked for her advice.

20. Let me read aloud a few _____ from the newspaper review of the new movie.

Writing: Words in Action

1. Look back at "Greetings from the WPA" (pages 12–13). Think about how people become resourceful when times get difficult. What binds people together during tough times? What sacrifices do they make? Write a letter to a friend, describing how you have overcome a difficult time. Write two or three paragraphs, using at least two details from the passage and three Unit words.

2. Do you think that teens should be expected to pitch in by getting jobs or doing chores or volunteer work? Why or why not? Write a brief essay in which you support your opinion with specific examples from your observations, studies, reading (refer to pages 12–13), or personal experience. Write at least three paragraphs, and use three or more words from this Unit.

Vocabulary in Context

Literary Text

The following excerpts are from The Scarlet Pimpernel *by Baroness Orczy. Some of the words you have studied in this Unit appear in **boldface** type. Complete each statement below the excerpt by circling the letter of the correct answer.*

1. And that was the whole story. It seemed so simple! and Marguerite could but marvel at the wonderful ingenuity, the boundless pluck and audacity which had **evolved** and helped to carry out this daring plan.

   When something has **evolved**, it has
   a. collapsed
   b. progressed
   c. resisted
   d. profited

2. It was distinctly more fitting to his newborn dignity to be as rude as possible; it was a sure sign of **servility** to meekly reply to civil questions.

   A state of **servility** suggests
   a. disappointment
   b. gratification
   c. submissiveness
   d. watchfulness

3. "There's all them Frenchy devils over the Channel yonder a-murderin' their king and nobility, and Mr. Pitt and Mr. Fox and Mr. Burke a-fightin' and a-**wranglin'** between them, if we Englishmen should 'low them to go on in their ungodly way."

   The act of **wrangling** involves
   a. squabbling
   b. fibbing
   c. lingering
   d. agreeing

   Actor Leslie Howard stars in the classic 1934 film version of *The Scarlet Pimpernel.*

4. Both the young men looked a little haggard and anxious, but otherwise they were irreproachably dressed, and there was not the slightest sign, about their courtly demeanour, of the terrible catastrophe, which they must have felt **hovering** round them and round their chief.

   Something that is **hovering** is NOT
   a. hanging
   b. possible
   c. lingering
   d. distant

5. Fate had willed it so. Marguerite, torn by the most terrible conflict the heart of woman can ever know, had resigned herself to its **decrees**. But Armand must be saved at any cost; he, first of all, for he was her brother, had been mother, father, friend to her ever since she, a tiny babe, had lost both her parents.

   Decrees are
   a. ideas
   b. verdicts
   c. praise
   d. promises

Interactive Quiz

Snap the code, or go to
vocabularyworkshop.com

*Read the following passage, taking note of the **boldface** words and their contexts. These words are among those you will be studying in Unit 2. As you complete the exercises in this Unit, it may help to refer to the way the words are used below.*

Instant Cash!
<Expository Essay>

Who can imagine life today without an Automated Teller Machine (ATM)? They are available in **bountiful** numbers throughout the world. Yet that virtually indispensible dispenser of cash is less than half a century old!

The first mechanical cash dispenser was the brainchild of an **enterprising** Turkish-American inventor, Luther George Simjian. His 200 patents included devices such as flight simulators, a meat tenderizer, and self-posing portrait cameras. When the idea of an automated banking machine struck him, he registered 20 patents before any bank agreed to give it a trial run. It is easy to assume that the inventor of such a popular machine was laughing all the way to the bank. Simjian's cash machine, however, did not prove **durable**. Within six months

Luther George Simjian

of its installation in New York City in 1939, the device was removed due to lack of customer acceptance.

It was not until 1967, nearly thirty years later, that Barclays Bank, in a **gingerly** launch, cautiously rolled out a self-service machine in London, England, that proved successful. The mechanism was relatively primitive, at least by today's standards. The first cash machines relied on customers' use of prepaid tokens to retrieve envelopes with a fixed amount of cash inside.

Soon afterwards, many other banks became **avowed** champions of the cash machine. The banks' ostensible rationale was customer service. But it would be foolish to **minimize** the many advantages that cash machines proffered to the banks themselves. By the late 1970s, the highest fixed cost for the average large bank was its branches. The greatest variable cost and **detriment** to profits were its staff. Cash deposits and cash withdrawals accounted for a veritable **glut** of a typical bank's transactions. With their perennially **frugal** eye, bank accountants swiftly recognized that self-service operations could reduce branch staff costs by 70 percent.

Experts quickly determined that public acceptance of ATMs pivoted on convenience, simplicity, speed, security, and trust. Location, in particular, was a key factor. For maximum efficiency, ATMs had to be located near public transport or in a shopping mall, not at a branch. The busier and more **congested** the location, apparently, the better. Now, roughly 75 percent of all cash dispensed by banks to their customers comes from cash machines. Devices that were originally spurned by the public are now **venerated** as essential institutions. Public acceptance of deposits by machine was significantly slower than customers' usage of ATMs for withdrawals. In general, it seems that customers still prefer and trust an over-the-counter transaction for deposits.

The future of the ATM seems assured. However, cash machines pose some interesting, unanswered questions. Will banks succeed, for example, in persuading their customers to **veer** away from long-ingrained habits and to utilize ATMs as often for deposits as for withdrawals? Will banks develop **oblique** advertising pitches, ingeniously slotted into the ATM program and calculated to exploit revenue opportunities?

Bank customers wait in line for a teller.

And what about security? An intriguing option is the issue of biometrics for customer identification. Everyone today knows about the problem of passwords. There are simply too many of them in people's lives. So the possibility that customers will be able to identify themselves at the neighborhood ATM by, say, using a fingerprint on the screen or through face recognition (biometrics) might herald a real improvement. Biometrics will most likely **invalidate** the cunning plans of **wanton** impostors. Now firmly established, ATMs may have an interesting future ahead of them.

For iWords and audio passages, snap the code, or go to **vocabularyworkshop.com**.

Technology scan of a man's hand

Definitions

Note the spelling, pronunciation, part(s) of speech, and definition(s) of each of the following words. Then write the appropriate form of the word in the blank spaces in the illustrative sentence(s) following. Finally, study the lists of synonyms and antonyms.

1. antics
(an' tiks)

(*n. pl.*) ridiculous and unpredictable behavior or actions

The _____ of the chimpanzees amused the crowds at the zoo.

SYNONYMS: pranks, shenanigans

2. avowed
(ə vaud')

(*adj., part.*) declared openly and without shame, acknowledged

The governor was an _____ supporter of the plan to aid public libraries throughout the state.

SYNONYMS: admitted, sworn
ANTONYMS: unacknowledged, undisclosed

3. banter
(ban' tər)

(*v.*) to exchange playful remarks, tease; (*n.*) talk that is playful and teasing

There is nothing my friends and I enjoy more than to _____ good-naturedly for hours.

Casual _____ helps to pass the time during a long journey.

SYNONYMS: (*n.*) raillery, chitchat
ANTONYM: (*n.*) serious talk

4. bountiful
(baunt' i fəl)

(*adj.*) giving freely, generous; plentiful, given abundantly

On Thanksgiving Day, people all over America celebrate the _____ gifts of nature.

SYNONYMS: liberal, abundant, copious
ANTONYMS: scarce, scanty, in short supply

5. congested
(kən jest' id)

(*adj., part.*) overcrowded, filled or occupied to excess

The doctor grew very concerned when the patient's lungs became _____ with fluid.

SYNONYMS: jammed, choked, packed
ANTONYMS: uncluttered, unimpeded

6. detriment
(det' rə mənt)

(*n.*) harm or loss; injury, damage; a disadvantage; a cause of harm, injury, loss, or damage

The home team survived a six-game losing streak with almost no _____ to its standing in the league.

SYNONYMS: hindrance, liability
ANTONYMS: advantage, help, plus

7. durable
(dûr′ ə bəl)

(*adj.*) sturdy, not easily worn out or destroyed; lasting for a long time; (*n. pl.*) consumer goods used repeatedly over a series of years

Denim is a very _____ kind of fabric.

Many people own household _____ such as furniture and appliances.

SYNONYMS: (*adj.*) long-lasting, enduring
ANTONYMS: (*adj.*) fragile, perishable, fleeting, ephemeral

8. enterprising
(ent′ ər prī ziŋ)

(*adj.*) energetic, willing and able to start something new; showing boldness and imagination

An _____ young person may turn a hobby into a way of earning money.

SYNONYMS: vigorous, aggressive, audacious
ANTONYMS: lazy, indolent, timid, diffident

9. frugal
(frü′ gəl)

(*adj.*) economical, avoiding waste and luxury; scanty, poor, meager

At home, we usually prepare _____ but nourishing and delicious meals.

SYNONYMS: thrifty, skimpy; ANTONYMS: wasteful, indulgent, lavish

10. gingerly
(jin′ jər lē)

(*adj., adv.*) with extreme care or caution

Difficult and demanding customers should be handled in a _____ and courteous manner.

Pedestrians made their way _____ along the slippery, snow-covered streets.

SYNONYMS: (*adv.*) cautiously, warily, circumspectly
ANTONYMS: (*adv.*) firmly, confidently, aggressively

11. glut
(glət)

(*v.*) to provide more than is needed or wanted; to feed or fill to the point of overstuffing; (*n.*) an oversupply

Hollywood studios _____ theaters with big-budget action movies during the summer season.

When there is a _____ of gasoline on the market, prices at the pump may drop dramatically.

SYNONYMS: (*v.*) flood, inundate; (*n.*) surplus, plethora
ANTONYMS: (*n.*) shortage, scarcity, dearth, paucity

12. incognito
(in käg nē′ tō)

(*adj., adv.*) in a disguised state, under an assumed name or identity; (*n.*) the state of being disguised; a person in disguise

Just before the battle of Agincourt, Shakespeare's King Henry V prowls through his camp _____.

In a way, makeup artists are practitioners of the fine art of

_____.

ANTONYM: (*adj.*) undisguised

13. invalidate
(in val′ ə dāt)

(v.) to make valueless, take away all force or effect

Lawyers will try to _____ the contract.

SYNONYMS: cancel, annul, disapprove, discredit
ANTONYMS: support, confirm, back up, legalize

14. legendary
(lej′ ən der ē)

(adj.) described in well-known stories; existing in old stories (legends) rather than in real life

Ajax was one of the _____ Greek heroes who fought before the walls of Troy.

SYNONYMS: mythical, fabulous, famous

15. maim
(mām)

(v.) to cripple, disable, injure, mar, disfigure, mutilate

Each year, accidental falls _____ thousands of people, some of them for life.

16. minimize
(min′ ə mīz)

(v.) to make as small as possible, make the least of; to make smaller than before

Whenever you are in a car, you should wear your seatbelt to _____ the risk of injury in an accident.

SYNONYMS: belittle, downplay
ANTONYMS: magnify, enlarge, exaggerate

17. oblique
(ō blēk′)

(adj.) slanting or sloping; not straightforward or direct

The boxer's _____ blow left his opponent unscathed.

SYNONYMS: diagonal, indirect
ANTONYMS: direct, straight to the point

18. veer
(vēr)

(v.) to change direction or course suddenly, turn aside, shift

The huge storm finally _____ out to sea, leaving much destruction in its wake.

19. venerate
(ven′ ə rāt)

(v.) to regard with reverence, look up to with great respect

In a number of cultures, it is customary for people to _____ the oldest members of society.

SYNONYMS: worship, revere, idolize
ANTONYMS: despise, detest, ridicule, deride

20. wanton
(wänt′ ən)

(adj.) reckless; heartless, unjustifiable; loose in morals; (n.) a spoiled, pampered person; one with low morals

The brave superhero soon put a stop to the evil villain's acts of _____ cruelty.

The main character in the popular miniseries was a charming but heartless _____.

SYNONYMS: (adj.) rash, malicious, spiteful, unprovoked
ANTONYMS: (adj.) justified, morally strict, responsible

Choosing the Right Word

Select the **boldface** word that better completes each sentence. You might refer to the passage on pages 22–23 to see how most of these words are used in context.

1. The mad Roman emperor Caligula believed that he was a god and expected people to (**venerate, veer**) him.

2. Our friendship has proved to be (**enterprising, durable**) because it is based on mutual respect and honesty.

3. I didn't want Charlotte to know that I was watching her, but occasionally I managed to steal a few (**oblique, legendary**) glances at her.

4. When they saw that they had been caught red-handed, they resorted to all kinds of (**detriments, antics**) in a vain attempt to prove their "innocence."

5. It was bad taste on your part to use that (**venerating, bantering**) tone when we were discussing such a sad event.

Bust of the notorious Roman emperor Caligula.

6. As a(n) (**avowed, gingerly**) supporter of women's rights, she believes that men and women should receive the same pay if they do the same jobs.

7. I will not try to (**minimize, banter**) the difficulties we face, but I am sure that we can overcome them by working together.

8. Although I love sports, I sometimes feel that television is becoming (**maimed, glutted**) with athletic events of all kinds.

9. After living for so long on a (**frugal, durable**) diet, I was amazed when I saw the variety of rich dishes served at the banquet.

10. Imagine our surprise when we found a trunk full of albums recorded by the (**legendary, incognito**) performer Ray Charles.

11. We are grateful for the (**frugal, bountiful**) legacy that our great artists and composers have given us.

12. April wrapped her puppy's wound (**gingerly, obliquely**) to avoid causing the pup any more pain.

13. Why do you suppose someone whose face is known all over the world would want to travel (**obliquely, incognito**)?

14. Detectives turn off the lights and use soft beams at the scene of a crime, as evidence is easier to see in (**wanton, oblique**) lighting.

15. Instead of just waiting for things to get better by themselves, we must be more (**legendary, enterprising**) in working for improvements.

16. We were shocked by their (**bountiful, wanton**) misuse of the money their parents had left them.

17. Self-confidence is a good quality; but if it is carried too far, it can be a (**detriment, glut**) to success in life.

18. Because of his repeated traffic violations, his driver's license has been (**congested, invalidated**).

19. Orders for (**enterprising, durable**) goods such as computers and cell phones were up this year, thanks to a recent boost in our economy.

20. Your speech would have been better if you had stayed with your main idea instead of (**veering, bantering**) off to side issues.

21. The (**legendary, wanton**) deeds of Sherlock Holmes are so well known that many people think he really lived.

22. Children may be (**maimed, avowed**) in spirit as well as in body if they do not have a secure and loving home environment.

23. Instead of approaching him timidly and (**frugally, gingerly**), tell him frankly what is on your mind.

24. Building a new skyscraper there will bring thousands of additional people into an area that is already (**invalidated, congested**).

25. The politician tried to (**venerate, minimize**) his role in the cover-up.

Synonyms

*Choose the word from this Unit that is the same or most nearly the same in meaning as the **boldface** word or expression in the phrase. Write that word on the line. Use a dictionary if necessary.*

1. the child prodigy's **celebrated** talent _____

2. laughed at the **tomfoolery** of the comedian _____

3. **swerved** to avoid a pothole _____

4. cared for those **wounded** in the fire _____

5. a **confirmed** opponent of higher taxes _____

6. annoyed by an **excess** of junk mail _____

7. **joked** with my teammates after the game _____

8. **underrated** the importance of the discovery _____

9. made **ambitious** plans for the company _____

10. a need to remain **anonymous** _____

Antonyms

*Choose the word from this Unit that is most nearly opposite in meaning to the **boldface** word or expression in the phrase. Write that word on the line. Use a dictionary if necessary.*

1. an animal that has been **healed**   _____

2. **solemn behavior** required at the service   _____

3. a witness who testifies **openly**   _____

4. gave the children a **stern lecture**   _____

5. a diary written by an **unknown** source   _____

Completing the Sentence

From the words in this Unit, choose the one that best completes each of the following sentences. Write the correct word form in the space provided.

1. Instead of walking straight from the farmhouse to the road, we set off in a(n) _____ direction across the field.

2. We should be willing to share our _____ food supplies with less fortunate people in other parts of the world.

3. The vandals broke windows, overturned desks, and left the school a scene of _____ destruction.

4. As Americans, we _____ the great ideals of human freedom expressed in the Bill of Rights.

5. The film star traveled _____ in order to avoid the attention of her adoring fans.

6. I was afraid of banging my bare feet against the furniture, so I walked through the darkened room very _____.

7. An inability to get along smoothly and effectively with other people will be a great _____ to you in any career you may choose.

8. We desperately needed every bit of help we could find, but what we got was a(n) _____ of advice and a scarcity of cold cash.

9. Although he had been severely _____ in the automobile accident, he was determined to return to his job and lead a normal life.

10. His income was small, but his _____ living habits enabled him to save a large sum of money over the years.

11. While I do not wish to alarm you, I will not _____ the danger if you refuse to have the entire herd vaccinated.

12. Even the most _____ materials will in time be damaged by flowing water.

13. To avoid the children in the street, the truck _____ sharply to the right and sideswiped several parked cars.

14. Davy Crockett was a real person, but so many tall tales have been told about him that he has become a(n) _____ figure.

15. In American law, the fact that the person accused of a crime is poor does not _____ his or her right to adequate legal representation.

16. Although she tried to cover it up with lively _____, I could see that her feelings had been deeply hurt.

17. We admired the _____ immigrant who set up a small shop and developed it into a large and prosperous business.

18. I would never have expected members of the senior class to take part in such childish _____!

19. What a change from the _____ streets of the inner city to the wide-open spaces of the Great Plains!

20. Isn't it strange for a(n) _____ music lover to show no interest in our school orchestra?

Writing: Words in Action

1. Look back at "Instant Cash!" (pages 22–23). Suppose you work for an advertising agency. A bank has asked you to create a commercial promoting the use of its ATM. Your ad copy should include at least two details from the passage and three Unit words to support your position.

2. Many people send texts or emails instead of speaking directly to others. Some people believe that, as a result, the art of conversation is declining. They fear people are losing their communication skills and replacing human interaction with superficial contacts through social media or by interacting with machines that have replaced human workers. Do you agree or disagree? In a brief essay, support your opinion with specific examples from your observations, studies, personal experience, or the reading (refer to pages 22–23). Write at least three paragraphs, and use three or more words from this Unit.

Vocabulary in Context

Literary Text

The following excerpts are from The Trimmed Lamp and Other Stories of the Four Million *by O. Henry. Some of the words you have studied in this Unit appear in* **boldface** *type. Complete each statement below the excerpt by circling the letter of the correct answer.*

1. "Are you going to Coney Island?" asked Blinker.

   "Me?" She turned upon him wide-open eyes full of **bantering** surprise. "Why, what a question! Can't you see that I'm riding a bicycle in the park?" ("Brickdust Row")

   Bantering exchanges are most likely
   a. ill-mannered
   b. uncaring
   c. secretive
   d. good-humored

2. The steamer **veered** as if to seek midstream, and then yawed, seemed to increase its speed and struck the Coney boat on the side near the stern, cutting into it with a terrifying shock and crash. ("Brickdust Row")

   If something has **veered**, it has
   a. changed directions
   b. moved forward
   c. stopped suddenly
   d. turned over

3. For Stuffy Pete was overcharged with the caloric produced by a super-**bountiful** dinner, beginning with oysters and ending with plum pudding, and including (it seemed to him) all the roast turkey and baked potatoes and chicken salad and squash pie and ice cream in the world. ("Two Thanksgiving Day Gentlemen")

   A **bountiful** dinner is definitely NOT
   a. delicious
   b. expensive
   c. lacking
   d. abundant

Portrait of William Sydney Porter, who wrote under the name "O. Henry"

4. And now for the story which is to prove to you that we have traditions on this side of the ocean that are becoming older at a much rapider rate than those of England are—thanks to our git-up and **enterprise**. ("Two Thanksgiving Day Gentlemen")

   The people in a country described as having **enterprise** are
   a. arrogant
   b. forgiving
   c. unusual
   d. ambitious

5. In this atmosphere Nancy belonged; and she throve in it and ate her **frugal** meals and schemed over her cheap dresses with a determined and contented mind. ("The Trimmed Lamp")

   Something that is **frugal** is
   a. sensible
   b. rare
   c. bland
   d. extravagant

Interactive Quiz

Snap the code, or go to **vocabularyworkshop.com**

*Read the following passage, taking note of the **boldface** words and their contexts. These words are among those you will be studying in Unit 3. As you complete the exercises in this Unit, it may help to refer to the way the words are used below.*

Grand Columbian Carnival Unites the World

<Press Release>

FOR IMMEDIATE RELEASE

World's Columbian Exposition to Open

Chicago Rolls Out Red Carpet for World Visitors

Chicago, Illinois—Drum roll, please! After years of **prodigious** preparation and immense hard work, the World's Columbian Exposition, celebrating the 400th anniversary of Christopher Columbus's landing in America, opens to the public on May 1, 1893. It's spectacular! It's **audacious**! It's like nothing you've ever seen before!

Come one, come all, and experience the great World's Fair on the shores of Lake Michigan. President Grover Cleveland will be on hand to officially cut the ribbon.

Hundreds of thousands of electric lightbulbs will light up the night sky and illuminate the buildings. There will be exhibits from each state in the union and from many foreign countries that show the **relevant** inventions, achievements, and wares of each. Commercial, agricultural, scientific, and artistic industries will be represented. Flags of the world will be **tethered** together in harmony. It promises to be the greatest monument to human progress witnessed thus far.

But the Fair will offer much more than homage to hard work and ingenuity. The organizers have **amassed** a plethora of captivating sideshows and entertainment. The Midway Plaisance has been **allotted** as the site for musical reviews and street buskers, dancing, and carnival rides— including Mr. George Ferris's magnificent Chicago Wheel, standing 250 feet tall and offering a bird's-eye view of the Fair.

There is sailing on the lake and lagoons, and gondola rides on the Venetian waterways and canals. A long, moving sidewalk along the lakefront pier will take you to the casino—for just a nickel a ticket! Norway is sending a life-sized model of a Viking ship, and the Liberty Bell is traveling from Philadelphia aboard a flatbed rail car. Pyrotechnics and fireworks will herald the arrival of a replica of Columbus's vessels from Spain. Plus, the Hall of Agriculture will feature an 11-ton "Monster Cheese" sent by Canada and a 1,500-pound chocolate Venus de Milo (no sampling allowed!).

Postcard depicting an aerial view of the World's Columbian Exposition

New York, St. Louis, Washington, D.C., and our own hometown **vied** for the honor of hosting the exposition, and Chicago won. Some were **skittish**: Could Chicago pull it off? After the city suffered such devastating losses in the Great Fire two decades earlier, skeptics voiced concern. One wag said the choice of Chicago was "as mad as a March hare." And while it is true that planners **grappled** with delays, bad weather, and **myriad** logistical nightmares, prominent leaders and ordinary citizens worked in **unison** to make the exposition a success.

An **elite** group of top architects led by Daniel Burnham designed the 200 magnificent exposition buildings. These designers chose a classical architectural theme, which vexed and **perturbed** a few **willful** modernist planners but pleased the majority. Renowned landscape designer Frederick Law Olmsted—creator of New York's lush Central Park—laid out the fairgrounds at Jackson Park, and it will be a most welcome addition to the city's panorama.

From our **perspective** (admittedly biased!), the Windy City is the perfect choice to host world visitors and celebrate our age of innovation and prosperity. The discovery of America deserves a splendid commemoration, and all indications point to a grand triumph!

The Great Wheel designed by George Ferris will debut at the exposition.

For the ladies, an added enticement is The Women's Building, designed by Miss Sophie Hayden, who graduated from Massachusetts Institute of Technlogy with a degree in architecture—the only woman to date to do so. And the Horticultural Hall is a paradise of exotic plants and flowers. Also not to be missed: The Court of Honor, at the center of the expo, known as the White City for its luminous white buildings.

The Court of Honor and the Statue of the Republic (nicknamed "Big Mary")

For iWords and audio passages, snap the code, or go to vocabularyworkshop.com.

Definitions

Note the spelling, pronunciation, part(s) of speech, and definition(s) of each of the following words. Then write the appropriate form of the word in the blank spaces in the illustrative sentence(s) following. Finally, study the lists of synonyms and antonyms.

1. allot
(ə lät′)

(*v.*) to assign or distribute in shares or portions

The teacher _____ books and supplies to each student on the first day of school.

SYNONYMS: apportion, parcel out, allocate

2. amass
(ə mas′)

(*v.*) to bring together, collect, gather, especially for oneself; to come together, assemble

A prudent investor can _____ a fortune in the stock market over the long run.

SYNONYMS: pile up, garner
ANTONYMS: scatter, dissipate, squander, waste

3. audacious
(ô dā′ shəs)

(*adj.*) bold, adventurous, recklessly daring

The audience cheered the _____ feats of the trapeze artists.

SYNONYMS: enterprising, brave
ANTONYMS: timid, cowardly

4. comply
(kəm plī′)

(*v.*) to yield to a request or command

Employees who fail to _____ with a company's rules may lose their jobs.

SYNONYMS: consent, acquiesce
ANTONYMS: reject, refuse, decline

5. devoid
(di void′)

(*adj.*) not having or using, lacking

The old well on my grandparents' property has long been _____ of water.

SYNONYMS: wanting, bereft
ANTONYMS: full, abounding

6. elite
(ā lēt′)

(*n.*) the choice part of a group of people or things; (*adj.*) superior

Each year, the social _____ of the community sponsors several events to benefit local charities.

You can get a fine education regardless of whether you attend an _____ school.

SYNONYMS: (*n.*) cream of the crop, upper crust
ANTONYMS: (*n.*) rank and file, dregs of society

7. grapple
(grap' əl)

(*n.*) an iron hook used to grab and hold; (*v.*) to come to grips with, wrestle or fight with

A ship equipped with _____ may be used to recover large pieces of wreckage from the ocean floor.

Store employees _____ with the thieves and held them until the police arrived.

SYNONYMS: (*v.*) tackle, confront, struggle with

8. incapacitate
(in kə pas' ə tāt)

(*v.*) to deprive of strength or ability; to make legally ineligible

In the 1940s and 1950s, polio _____ many thousands of people each year all over the world.

SYNONYMS: debilitate, paralyze, cripple
ANTONYMS: rehabilitate, renew

9. instigate
(in' stə gāt)

(*v.*) to urge on; to stir up, start, incite

Several demonstrators in the angry crowd did their best to _____ a riot.

ANTONYMS: stop, quell, squelch, quash

10. longevity
(län jev' ə tē)

(*n.*) long life, long duration, length of life

The sea turtle is known for its _____.

ANTONYMS: shortness, transience

11. myriad
(mir' ē əd)

(*adj.*) in very great numbers; (*n.*) a very great number

Scientists continue to make new discoveries in their studies of the _____ life-forms of the jungle.

You will find information about a _____ of subjects on the Internet.

SYNONYMS: (*adj.*) innumerable, countless
ANTONYMS: (*adj.*) few, scant, sparse

12. perspective
(pər spek' tiv)

(*n.*) a point of view or general standpoint from which different things are viewed, physically or mentally; the appearance to the eye of various objects at a given time, place, or distance

The designs for the children's playhouse were drawn to scale and in the right _____.

SYNONYMS: viewpoint, sense of proportion

13. perturb
(pər tərb')

(*v.*) to trouble, make uneasy; to disturb greatly; to throw into confusion

The rude and disruptive behavior of several party guests _____ the host and hostess.

SYNONYMS: upset, agitate, anger
ANTONYMS: delight, gladden, please

14. prodigious
(prə dij' əs)

(*adj.*) immense; extraordinary in bulk, size, or degree

Few intellects have rivaled the _____ mind of Albert Einstein.

SYNONYMS: gigantic, tremendous, astounding
ANTONYMS: puny, minuscule, insignificant

15. relevant
(rel' ə vənt)

(*adj.*) connected with or related to the matter at hand

I found several Web sites that provided information _____ to the topic of my research paper.

SYNONYMS: pertinent, germane, applicable
ANTONYMS: unconnected, extraneous

16. skittish
(skit' ish)

(*adj.*) extremely nervous and easily frightened; shy or timid; extremely cautious; unstable, undependable

Only an experienced and confident rider should mount a _____ horse.

SYNONYMS: jumpy, restive, capricious, fickle
ANTONYMS: bold, daring, reckless, cool, unflappable

17. tether
(teth' er)

(*n.*) a rope or chain used to fasten something to a fixed object; the outer limit of strength or resources; (*v.*) to fasten with a rope or chain

Some young people find it difficult to break the emotional and financial _____ that bind them to their parents.

Before the storm, I _____ the boat securely to the dock.

SYNONYMS: (*v.*) tie up, chain up, leash
ANTONYMS: (*v.*) untie, let loose

18. unison
(yü' nə sən)

(*n.*) a sounding together; agreement or accord

The members of our new student orchestra need to practice playing in _____.

SYNONYMS: harmony, concord, assent

19. vie
(vī)

(*v.*) to compete; to strive for victory or superiority

Many actors _____ for the leading role in the famous director's new film.

SYNONYMS: contend, rival

20. willful
(wil' fəl)

(*adj.*) stubbornly self-willed; done on purpose, deliberate

After lengthy deliberations, the jury found the defendant guilty of _____ murder.

SYNONYMS: headstrong, obstinate, premeditated
ANTONYMS: docile, obedient, tractable

Choosing the Right Word

Select the **boldface** word that better completes each sentence. You might refer to the passage on pages 32–33 to see how most of these words are used in context.

1. Jane Addams was not only profoundly (**perturbed, instigated**) by the suffering of other people but also tried hard to help them.

2. Great new discoveries in science can be made only by men and women with intellectual (**compliance, audacity**).

3. He has had such bad experiences with motorcycles that he has become extremely (**audacious, skittish**) of them.

4. If we have to share the same locker, please try to keep your things in the space (**allotted, amassed**) to you.

Jane Addams opened Hull House, a settlement house in Chicago.

5. Perhaps in the long-term (**longevity, perspective**) of history, some events that seem very important now will prove to be minor.

6. She had devoted her life to (**amassing, minimizing**) not material riches but the love, respect, and thanks of every member of this community.

7. She delivered a simple, low-key speech, completely (**devoid, relevant**) of fancy language or emotional appeals.

8. My neighbor has all kinds of colorful kites and wind socks (**devoid, tethered**) to stakes in her yard, claiming that they keep the deer from eating her plants.

9. The bitter strike closed shops, shut down factories, and (**incapacitated, allotted**) an entire industry for months.

10. The defense has told you about the defendant's unhappy childhood, but how is this (**relevant, willful**) to the question of innocence or guilt?

11. Mr. Ponce knew that it was Tyler who blew the whistle in class, as Tyler is always (**amassing, instigating**) trouble.

12. I wonder why the camp directors were unwilling to (**comply, vie**) with my request to keep a pet snake in my tent.

13. How do you explain the fact that in practically every country the (**elite, longevity**) of women is greater than that of men?

14. (**Willful, Perturbed**) with her son's lazy ways, Ms. Lowry called the boy into the house, demanding that he clean up his room immediately.

15. As I glanced upward at the giant sequoia, I realized how (**prodigiously, audaciously**) tall these trees truly are.

16. We will never have a well-organized or effective club if all the members insist (**willfully, skittishly**) on having their own way.

17. As I stared at the luscious chocolate swirl cake, I bravely (**incapacitated, grappled**) with temptation—but the chocolate cake won!

18. People who come from rich and socially prominent families don't always belong to the intellectual (**myriad, elite**).

19. Our course in life sciences has given us some idea of the (**myriad, unison**) varieties of plants and animals inhabiting the earth.

20. I don't think anyone can hope to (**vie, perturb**) with Gloria in the election for "Most Popular Student."

21. Unless you want to (**amass, instigate**) a quarrel, don't make insulting remarks about my friends and family.

22. By the twentieth mile of a marathon, many runners have reached the end of their (**perspective, tether**).

23. Can you imagine what a (**relevant, prodigious**) amount of research is needed for a multivolume reference book such as the *Encyclopaedia Britannica*?

24. In the next chorus, *please* try to sing in (**unison, compliance**).

25. Do you really think your story is (**relevant, compliant**) to this conversation?

 **Synonyms**

*Choose the word from this Unit that is the same or most nearly the same in meaning as the **boldface** word or expression in the phrase. Write that word on the line. Use a dictionary if necessary.*

1. environment **deficient in** water resources　　　＿＿＿＿＿＿＿＿＿＿

2. repeated delays that **irritated** the passengers　　＿＿＿＿＿＿＿＿＿＿

3. seems determined to **provoke** an argument　　　＿＿＿＿＿＿＿＿＿＿

4. **doled out** four tickets to each member of the cast　＿＿＿＿＿＿＿＿＿＿

5. **accumulated** a huge collection of folk art　　　　＿＿＿＿＿＿＿＿＿＿

6. **submit to** the terms of the treaty　　　　　　　＿＿＿＿＿＿＿＿＿＿

7. arrived at **consensus** on the course of action　　＿＿＿＿＿＿＿＿＿＿

8. chose only the **select few**　　　　　　　　　　＿＿＿＿＿＿＿＿＿＿

9. bred for their **endurance**　　　　　　　　　　　＿＿＿＿＿＿＿＿＿＿

10. an illness that **disables** young and old alike　　＿＿＿＿＿＿＿＿＿＿

Antonyms

*Choose the word from this Unit that is most nearly opposite in meaning to the **boldface** word or expression in the phrase. Write that word on the line. Use a dictionary if necessary.*

1. called in to **suppress** the protestors

   _____

2. a river **teeming with** fish

   _____

3. left the army **restored**

   _____

4. arrested for **disobeying** the law

   _____

5. the **brevity** of the public's interest in the story

   _____

Completing the Sentence

From the words in this Unit, choose the one that best completes each of the following sentences. Write the correct word form in the space provided.

1. Trying to navigate through rush-hour traffic on a high-speed expressway can be a nightmare for a(n) _____ driver.

2. You will have to use a(n) _____ to recover the lobster trap from the bottom of the bay.

3. I am completely _____ of sympathy for anyone who loses a job because of carelessness and indifference.

4. In wartime, it is not unusual for secret agents to be sent behind enemy lines in an effort to _____ a rebellion.

5. If all the members of the cast work in _____, I am sure we will have a successful class show.

6. I know that you are a brilliant student, but I am still amazed that you could _____ such a vast store of information so quickly.

7. Though we have made many outstanding contributions to the conquest of space, landing men on the moon is probably our most _____ achievement.

8. He joined the _____ group of athletes who have run a mile in under four minutes.

9. Before we set out on the camping trip, our Scout leader _____ special tasks and responsibilities to each one of us.

10. The _____ child insisted on wearing sneakers to her sister's wedding.

11. Someday, when you see this event in its proper _____, you will realize that it is not as important as it seems now.

12. The disease had so _____ the poor woman that she was no longer able to leave her bed.

13. The autumn night sky, with its _____stars, always fills me with awe and wonder.

14. We can thank modern medical science for the increased _____ of human beings in most parts of the world.

15. Dad said, "I am _____ not because you failed the exam, but because you seem unable to understand *why* you failed it."

16. I refuse to _____ with any order issued by a person who has absolutely no knowledge of the project I'm working on.

17. A number of cities _____ with one another to be chosen as the site of a national political convention.

18. When he seemed hopelessly defeated, General George Washington crossed the Delaware River and launched a(n) _____ surprise attack on the Hessians.

19. Since the town meeting tonight has been called to deal with conservation, only discussion _____ to that subject will be allowed.

20. There in the middle of the garden was a goat _____ to a stake.

Writing: Words in Action

1. Look back at "Grand Columbian Carnival Unites the World" (pages 32–33). Suppose that you are one of the sponsors for the exposition. You want to persuade visitors to attend this event. Write a brochure enticing visitors, using at least two details from the passage and three Unit words.

2. Suppose a World Exposition for the 21st century was held today. What kind of exhibits would reflect the ingenuity of our times? Write a brief essay in which you describe this event. In your conclusion, state whether you think such an event would help to bring unity to the world. Support your essay with specific examples from the reading (refer to pages 32–33) or from your observations, studies, or personal experience. Write at least three paragraphs, and use three or more words from this Unit.

Vocabulary in Context

Literary Text

The following excerpts are from Walden *by Henry David Thoreau. Some of the words you have studied in this Unit appear in* **boldface** *type. Complete each statement below the excerpt by circling the letter of the correct answer.*

1. Sometimes one [whip-poor-will] would circle round and round me in the woods a few feet distant as if **tethered** by a string, when probably I was near its eggs. They sang at intervals throughout the night, and were again as musical as ever just before and about dawn.

   If something is **tethered** it is NOT
   a. fastened   c. nearby
   b. free   d. caught

2. I called on the king, but he made me wait in his hall, and conducted like a man **incapacitated** for hospitality. There was a man in my neighborhood who lived in a hollow tree. His manners were truly regal. I should have done better had I called on him.

   A person who is **incapacitated** of a trait is
   a. filled with it   c. deprived of it
   b. concealed from it   d. suitable for it

3. To speak literally, a hundred Irishmen, with Yankee overseers, came from Cambridge every day to get out the ice. They divided it into cakes by methods too well known to require description, and these, being sledded to the shore, were rapidly hauled off on to an ice platform, and raised by **grappling** irons and block and tackle, worked by horses, on to a stack . . .

   An object described as **grappling**
   a. heaps   c. crushes
   b. grasps   d. hauls

Walden describes Thoreau's experience in the woods, where he built a cabin and lived for several years.

4. . . . I was surprised to find myself surrounded by **myriads** of small perch, about five inches long, of a rich bronze color in the green water, sporting there, and constantly rising to the surface and dimpling it, sometimes leaving bubbles on it.

   If there are **myriads** of fish, the fish are
   a. astonishing   c. admired
   b. multicolored   d. plentiful

5. Let us rise early and fast, or break fast, gently and without **perturbation**; let company come and let company go, let the bells ring and the children cry—determined to make a day of it.

   A **perturbation** is a(n)
   a. disturbance   c. question
   b. formality   d. agreement

Interactive Quiz

Snap the code, or go to **vocabularyworkshop.com**

Vocabulary for Comprehension

*Read the following passage in which some of the words you have studied in Units 1–3 appear in **boldface** type. Then answer the questions on page 43.*

This passage discusses the way ancient Native Americans built structures, such as pyramids, that have lasted for centuries.

(Line)

Long before Europeans reached the Americas, native people erected massive **citadels**. Many of these ancient buildings still stand,
(5) delighting and fascinating both scholars and tourists. But the durability of these structures raises puzzling questions. Many Native American civilizations arose in
(10) earthquake zones or near active volcanoes. All the structures built in these areas were subject to stresses that could easily have reduced them to **rubble**. What factors
(15) account for the **longevity** of these great monuments to Native American inventiveness and skill? Why have these structures survived while so many European-style buildings
(20) have not?

Because scholars have few written documents from this period to turn to, they must **grapple with** physical and cultural evidence. They
(25) compare the clues they find with what they know about modern architecture and building practices.

Scholars now believe that Native American architects knew
(30) the secrets of building durable structures on unstable ground. Inca masons, for example, found a way to fit large blocks of stone together snugly to form walls
(35) that were both strong and flexible, able to withstand tremors and quakes. The tapered shape of the temple pyramids was also a contributing factor. Many early
(40) architects understood that the combination of **oblique** angles and straight, parallel lines gives a building stability.

Comparison with European architecture provides another
(45) **perspective**. Unlike their European counterparts, Native American architects did not construct arches. The arch, widely used in European
(50) buildings to achieve height, is very vulnerable to stresses that can cause it to collapse. In contrast, most early Native American structures rose in height with the
(55) support of heavy, solid walls.

These elements may explain why so many of these superb structures remain for us to appreciate today.

1. The main purpose of the passage is to
   a. describe how the Inca built pyramids
   b. summarize the findings of ancient documents
   c. challenge scholars' theories about Native American structures
   d. explain why ancient Native American structures are still standing
   e. investigate why European buildings are superior to Native American structures

2. The meaning of **citadels** (line 3) is
   a. monuments
   b. apartments
   c. strongholds
   d. bridges
   e. malls

3. **Rubble** (line 14) most nearly means
   a. slums
   b. debris
   c. ashes
   d. nothing
   e. building blocks

4. **Longevity** (line 15) is best defined as
   a. long life
   b. long halls
   c. modern design
   d. timeless beauty
   e. lasting popularity

5. At the end of paragraph 1, the author poses two questions (lines 14–20) that
   a. are rarely discussed
   b. cannot be answered
   c. concern European scholars
   d. provide a focus for the rest of the passage
   e. puzzled ancient Native American architects

6. The meaning of **grapple with** (line 23) is
   a. doubt
   b. tackle
   c. ignore
   d. accept
   e. iron hook

7. In paragraph 3 (lines 28–43), the author speculates on why ancient Native American structures have withstood
   a. natural disasters
   b. hot, humid weather
   c. countless tribal wars
   d. snow, wind, and rain
   e. invasion by Europeans

8. From lines 28–43, you can infer that the type of natural disaster the Inca were most likely to experience was
   a. floods
   b. tornadoes
   c. volcanic eruptions
   d. hurricanes
   e. earthquakes

9. **Oblique** (line 41) most nearly means
   a. wide
   b. sharp
   c. unusual
   d. sloping
   e. straight

10. **Perspective** (line 46) is best defined as
    a. topic
    b. viewpoint
    c. argument
    d. variation
    e. theory

11. According to the author, Native American structures have all of the following architectural features EXCEPT
    a. arches
    b. stone walls
    c. pyramid shapes
    d. heavy, solid walls
    e. angles and parallel lines

12. The author's attitude toward ancient Native American builders is best described as one of
    a. criticism
    b. sympathy
    c. tolerance
    d. bewilderment
    e. admiration

Two-Word Completions

Select the pair of words that best completes the meaning of each of the following sentences.

1. The TV marathon not only garnered _____ amounts of money for Africa's starving millions but also yielded an unexpectedly rich _____ of publicity for their plight.
   a. myriad . . . rubble
   b. legendary . . . allotment
   c. prodigious . . . bonanza
   d. bountiful . . . banter

2. "If he weren't so rude, I'd be glad to _____ with him on the project," I said. "But I don't think I can work with someone who always behaves in such a _____ manner."
   a. wrangle . . . servile
   b. collaborate . . . churlish
   c. banter . . . relevant
   d. vie . . . congested

3. "A person has to expect a little accidental bumping and pushing in a crowded bus," I observed to my companion. "It's just not possible to avoid _____ another passenger when the center aisle is _____ with people."
   a. maiming . . . devoid
   b. grappling . . . elite
   c. minimizing . . . glutted
   d. jostling . . . congested

4. It isn't wise to give very young children toys that will break easily. They need playthings that are _____ because they haven't yet learned to handle fragile items _____.
   a. servile . . . churlishly
   b. durable . . . gingerly
   c. frugal . . . willfully
   d. prodigious . . . wantonly

5. He was a man of great energy and _____. In no time at all, he rose from relatively humble beginnings to the very _____ of power.
   a. enterprise . . . citadels
   b. compliance . . . perspectives
   c. longevity . . . antics
   d. audacity . . . durables

6. If you are careless with your money, you will always be penniless. But if you are _____, you may be able to _____ a sizable personal fortune.
   a. bountiful . . . evolve
   b. enterprising . . . maim
   c. frugal . . . amass
   d. audacious . . . preclude

7. The clownish _____ of cartoon characters, both animal and human, have won the hearts and _____ of many generations of delighted children.
   a. banter . . . bonanzas
   b. antics . . . plaudits
   c. adages . . . vigils
   d. tethers . . . decrees

Idioms

In the passage about the World's Columbian Exposition (see pages 32–33), the writer states that at least one person viewed the choice of Chicago as the host city as "mad as a March hare."

"Mad as a March hare" is an idiom that means "showing little reason" or "foolish." An **idiom** is a figure of speech; the words are not to be interpreted literally. Idioms are informal expressions that are unique to every language. Although idioms are colorful and expressive, they should be used sparingly in formal writing.

Choosing the Right Idiom

*Read each sentence. Use context clues to figure out the meaning of each idiom in **boldface** print. Then write the letter of the definition for the idiom in the sentence.*

1. Although Jack was in agonizing pain, he **kept a stiff upper lip** until the paramedics arrived. _____

2. There were so many sales that I was able to buy this dress **for a song**. _____

3. The boss thinks Eddie is a **bad egg**, and she wants me to watch him closely. _____

4. I've gone over the house **with a fine tooth comb**, and I can't find my ring anywhere. _____

5. Ms. Robins is **one smart cookie**, so she's not going to believe that the dog ate your homework. _____

6. My little nephews **fight like cats and dogs**, so I don't enjoy babysitting them. _____

7. Zander better expect to **pony up** if he wants to buy that fancy motorcycle. _____

8. The tutor was **banging his head against the wall** trying to explain algebra to me. _____

9. My best friend Brianna and I are always **on the same wavelength**. _____

10. Unfortunately, the plans for the new pedestrian bridge have been **put on ice**. _____

a. someone who can't be trusted

b. frustrated after several unsuccessful attempts

c. at a low price; for very little

d. pay or contribute some money

e. in agreement

f. postponed

g. acted bravely or showed no fear

h. bicker; argue intensely

i. someone who is not easy to deceive

j. in great detail; thoroughly

Writing with Idioms

Find the meaning of each idiom. (Use a dictionary if necessary.) Then write a sentence for each idiom.

1. get your feet wet

_____

2. eat your heart out

_____

3. hit the roof

_____

4. keep a straight face

_____

5. throw in the towel

_____

_____

6. iron in the fire

_____

_____

7. pull yourself up by your own bootstraps

_____

_____

8. make heads or tails of something

_____

9. got your number

_____

10. knock your socks off

_____

11. stick out your neck

_____

12. walk on clouds

_____

Denotation and Connotation

When you look up a word's meaning in the dictionary, you find the denotation. **Denotation** is the strict, literal definition of a word. The meaning is neutral.

However, many words also have **connotations**, or feelings or emotions that people associate with them. These feelings can be either positive or negative.

Consider these synonyms for the neutral word *bold*.

> *ambitious*   *enterprising*   *aggressive*   *pushy*

Ambitious and *enterprising* have positive connotations, whereas *aggressive* and *pushy* are negative.

> **Think:** Inventors are ambitious and enterprising, while a used car salesman is aggressive and pushy.

Look at these examples of words. Notice how the connotation of each word varies.

NEUTRAL	POSITIVE	NEGATIVE
watchful	vigilant	spying
statement	decree	ultimatum
durable	enduring	never-ending

Whether they are writing advertisements or novels, writers know that words can carry powerful emotions. By being aware of the power of connotations, or "shades of meaning," a reader can be more sensitive to the power of words to shape a message and elicit an emotional response. Not everyone reacts in an identical way to the same words, however. A skilled writer understands that some words can evoke either a positive or a negative emotion in different readers.

Shades of Meaning

Write a plus sign (+) in the box if the word has a positive connotation.
Write a minus sign (–) if the word has a negative connotation. Put a zero (0)
if the word is neutral.

1. adage ☐   **2.** glut ☐   **3.** bountiful ☐   **4.** congested ☐

5. bonanza ☐   **6.** allot ☐   **7.** excerpt ☐   **8.** wanton ☐

9. durable ☐   **10.** churlish ☐   **11.** oblique ☐   **12.** enterprising ☐

13. maim ☐   **14.** collaborate ☐   **15.** detriment ☐   **16.** unison ☐

Expressing the Connotation

Read each sentence. Select the word in parentheses that better expresses the connotation (positive, negative, or neutral) given at the beginning of the sentence.

positive **1.** I consider myself to be a (**frugal, stingy**) shopper and buy most of my clothes off-season.

negative **2.** People who had been waiting for hours were outraged when a man (**brushed against, jostled**) them on his way to the front of the line.

positive **3.** Given her (**daring, audacious**) approach to life, I'm not surprised she is always a topic of conversation!

neutral **4.** Did you see that car (**veer, turn**) into the other lane without signaling?

neutral **5.** Kathryn looks forward to book club meetings because she enjoys all the (**banter, conversation**).

positive **6.** Aunt Marla was excited to meet the (**legendary, well-known**) movie star.

neutral **7.** My mother is one of three local citizens who are (**vying, grasping**) for a seat on the school board.

negative **8.** When you act like a (**willful, rebellious**) child, people will not react positively toward you.

Challenge: Using Connotation

*Choose vocabulary words from Units 1–3 to replace the **boldface** words in the sentences below. Then explain how the connotation of the replacement word changes the tone of the sentence.*

servile	groping	skittish
incognito	tethered	prodigious

1. Tossed into a dark cell, the prisoner bumped around, **feeling** _____ for the walls and the door.

_____

_____

2. Not only was William Blake a **great** _____ poet, he was a talented artist as well.

_____

_____

3. Many of the animals that were typically playful and trusting became **bashful** _____ after the hurricane.

_____

_____

Classical Roots

vers, vert—to turn

This Latin root appears in **revert** (page 16), which means "to return, to go back to a previous, or lower, condition." Some other words based on the same root are listed below.

controversy	inverse	reversal	verse
conversant	pervert	traverse	vertiginous

From the list of words above, choose the one that corresponds to each of the brief definitions below. Write the word in the blank space in the illustrative sentence below the definition. Use a dictionary if necessary.

1. familiar by use or study; acquainted (*"turning with"*)

   Before we remodeled our house, we sought expert advice from someone _____ with the town's building code.

2. to turn away from the right course; to lead astray, distort (*"thoroughly, utterly turned"*)

   The defendant was accused of paying bribes to try to _____ the justice system.

3. a lengthy dispute (*"a turning against"*)

   A new development in medical technology may spark a heated _____ within the field.

4. to travel across; to cross and recross; to extend over

   We plan to _____ the countryside by bicycle this summer.

5. whirling or spinning; tending to make dizzy; affected by or suffering from dizziness

   The _____ rides in amusement parks are popular with children of all ages.

6. turned upside down or inside out; referring to a relationship in which one item increases as the other decreases

   Division is the _____ of multiplication.

7. a change or overthrow; a change of fortune (*usually for the worse*), setback

   The press criticized the Supreme Court's _____ of the state court's decision.

8. a line of poetry; poetic writing (*"a turning, as of a line"*)

   The teacher asked each student to recite a _____ of a favorite poem.

*Read the following passage, taking note of the **boldface** words and their contexts. These words are among those you will be studying in Unit 4. As you complete the exercises in this Unit, it may help to refer to the way the words are used below.*

Toni Cade Bambara

＜Author Profile＞

Toni Cade Bambara (1939–1995) wore many hats during her lifetime: writer, editor, teacher, filmmaker, activist, and social worker. Born in Harlem, she came of age during the civil rights movement and the stirrings of feminism. Bambara **deplored** social injustice. Her disapproval spurred her to work hard to **oust** injustice from American society. Her career united diverse interests in a single-minded effort to build and **bolster** equality and tolerance.

As a young woman, Bambara lived in New York City. She gained a faculty position at Livingston College, a new unit of Rutgers University designed to serve underprivileged students. She achieved academic recognition by editing the landmark anthology *The Black Woman* (1970). This collection featured poems, essays, and stories by stellar African American writers, including Alice Walker, Audre Lorde, and Nikki Giovanni. When one **peruses** the anthology today, it is hard to imagine that no one before Bambara had attempted such a project.

Two years later, Bambara **mustered** a group of short stories for her publication entitled *Gorilla, My Love*. It decisively **annulled** any doubt that Bambara was a major new voice in American fiction. The stylistic traits that her work was **prone** to are clearly visible: urban settings, first-person narrators, the theme of community, and an uncanny mastery of the spoken word. For Bambara, urban language was far from **frivolous**. Instead, she used it to plunge the reader into a real and edgy world. Bristling with sassy humor, Bambara's leading characters are often young black girls who refuse to knuckle under to prejudice or disrespect. Strong and self-reliant, they feel no **qualms** about talking back, as is shown by Squeaky, the narrator in one of Bambara's best-known stories, "Raymond's Run." Squeaky may not have been born on Easy Street, but as portrayed by Bambara, she possesses a wealth of wisdom and compassion at an early age.

During the 1970s and 1980s, Bambara **sustained** a hectic schedule of teaching, writing, and social and political activism. Her first novel, *The Salt Eaters* (1980), focuses on a fictional community organizer, Velma Henry. After suffering a nervous breakdown, Velma seeks **recourse** with an untraditional healer. In the novel, Bambara presents illness and pain as metaphors for social and political oppression. Health issues **obsess** many of the characters. The novel presents multiple perspectives and an intricate, experimental structure. *The Salt Eaters* won the American Book Award and the Langston Hughes Society Award in 1981.

During this period, Bambara was also active in documentary film work. Such films, she felt, could shake up indifferent viewers who had become **blasé** or **staid** about injustice and inequality. Her script for the film *The Bombing of Osage Avenue* (1986) received best documentary awards from the Pennsylvania Association of Broadcasters and the National Black Programming Consortium.

It was also during this period that Bambara began the novel that many critics consider her masterpiece: *Those Bones Are Not My Child*. Harrowing and suspenseful, the novel presents a city caught in the grip of political and racial tensions. Sadly, Bambara did not live to complete this work. She died of cancer on December 9, 1995. The Nobel Prize-winning novelist Toni Morrison, ever **solicitous** of her good friend Bambara, saw the book through to publication. Bambara's work remains popular and is often included in anthologies of notable stories for young adults.

Audio

For iWords and audio passages, snap the code, or go to **vocabularyworkshop.com**.

Definitions

Note the spelling, pronunciation, part(s) of speech, and definition(s) of each of the following words. Then write the appropriate form of the word in the blank spaces in the illustrative sentence(s) following. Finally, study the lists of synonyms and antonyms.

1. annul
(ə nəl')

(*v.*) to reduce to nothing; to make ineffective or inoperative; to declare legally invalid or void

The state legislators voted by an overwhelming majority to _____ the out-of-date law.

SYNONYMS: cancel, abolish, invalidate, nullify
ANTONYMS: validate, authorize, ratify

2. blasé
(blä zā')

(*adj.*) indifferent, bored as a result of having enjoyed many pleasures; apathetic

Battle-hardened soldiers may tend to become a bit _____ about the dangers they face.

ANTONYMS: enthusiastic, passionate, fervent

3. bolster
(bōl' stər)

(*v.*) to support, give a boost to; (*n.*) a long pillow or cushion; a supporting post

When you write a research paper, you should always use appropriate facts to _____ your case.

The sofa has four comfortable _____.

SYNONYMS: (*v.*) reinforce, buttress, validate
ANTONYMS: (*v.*) undermine, weaken, impair

4. deplore
(di plôr')

(*v.*) to feel or express regret or disapproval

Social critics _____ what they believe is a widespread decline in good manners.

SYNONYMS: lament, bemoan, bewail
ANTONYMS: approve, commend, extol

5. frivolous
(friv' ə ləs)

(*adj.*) of little importance, not worthy of serious attention; not meant seriously

I'll ignore your _____ suggestion.

SYNONYMS: silly, foolish, inane, petty
ANTONYMS: serious, important, significant

6. muster
(məs' tər)

(*v.*) to bring together for service or battle; to gather or summon; to amount to, comprise, include; (*n.*) a list of military personnel; a gathering, accumulation

You will need to _____ your courage to face the bully who has been tormenting you.

The sleepy new recruits assembled on the parade ground
for the early morning _____.

SYNONYMS: (*v.*) mobilize, marshal; (*n.*) roster, inventory
ANTONYMS: (*v.*) disband, dismiss, disperse

7. nonentity
(nän en′ tə tē)

(*n.*) a person or thing of no importance
We may not be movie stars, but we did not deserve to be
treated as _____ by the presumptuous
and haughty headwaiter.

SYNONYM: nobody
ANTONYM: celebrity

8. obsess
(äb ses′)

(*v.*) to trouble, haunt, or fill the mind
If you allow fear of failure to _____ you,
you will find it difficult or even impossible to achieve your
goals in life.

SYNONYM: preoccupy

9. ornate
(ôr nāt′)

(*adj.*) elaborately decorated; showily splendid
If you ask me, an _____ gilded frame
distracts the viewer's eye from a simple drawing.

SYNONYMS: fancy, flashy, flamboyant
ANTONYMS: plain, stark, austere

10. oust
(aůst)

(*v.*) to remove, drive out of a position or place
Military leaders _____ the duly elected
president and took over the government.

SYNONYMS: expel, eject
ANTONYMS: admit, welcome

11. peruse
(pə rüz′)

(*v.*) to read thoroughly and carefully
It is wise to have a lawyer _____ an
agreement before you sign it.

SYNONYMS: study, pore over, scrutinize

12. porous
(pôr′ əs)

(*adj.*) full of tiny holes; able to be penetrated by air or water
Some synthetic materials are as _____
and strong as natural sponges.

SYNONYMS: leaky, permeable
ANTONYMS: airtight, impermeable

13. promontory
(präm′ ən tôr ē)

(*n.*) a high point of land extending into water
We chose a high _____ overlooking the
sea as the perfect spot for our picnic lunch.

SYNONYMS: cliff, outcrop, jetty

14. prone
(prōn)

(*adj.*) lying face down; inclined, likely

Unfortunately, I am _____ to earaches and sinus infections.

SYNONYMS: prostrate, liable
ANTONYMS: standing upright, unlikely

15. qualm
(kwäm)

(*n.*) a pang of conscience, uneasiness, misgiving, or doubt; a feeling of faintness or nausea

Don't you have serious _____ about voting for such a relatively unknown and inexperienced candidate?

SYNONYMS: regret, second thought, scruple

16. recourse
(rē′ kôrs)

(*n.*) a person or thing turned to for help or advice; the act of seeking help or protection

If my letter of complaint fails to get results, I will still have _____ to a higher authority.

SYNONYMS: redress, remedy

17. residue
(rez′ ə dü)

(*n.*) a remainder, that which remains when a part has been used up or removed

A _____ of sticky taffy made the pan difficult to clean.

SYNONYMS: remnant, remains, leavings

18. solicitous
(sə lis′ ət əs)

(*adj.*) showing concern or care; fearful or anxious about someone or something

Neighbors made _____ inquiries about the state of the elderly couple's health.

SYNONYM: concerned
ANTONYMS: unconcerned, indifferent, apathetic

19. staid
(stād)

(*adj.*) serious and dignified; quiet or subdued in character or conduct

Many companies have a dress code which requires that all employees wear _____ colors such as navy or gray.

SYNONYMS: sedate, sober, prim
ANTONYMS: gaudy, jaunty, unconventional

20. sustain
(sə stān′)

(*v.*) to support, nourish, keep up; to suffer, undergo; to bear up under, withstand; to affirm the validity of

You may _____ a serious eye injury if you forget to wear your safety goggles when you work with chemicals or power tools.

SYNONYMS: foster, uphold

Choosing the Right Word

*Select the **boldface** word that better completes each sentence. You might refer to the passage on pages 50–51 to see how most of these words are used in context.*

1. Isn't it strange that a great American writer like Emily Dickinson was considered a (**nonentity, promontory**) in her own lifetime?

2. I admire the way Anne delivered a long, involved speech entirely without (**muster, recourse**) to written notes.

3. If you want to learn to play chess, I suggest that you begin by (**deploring, perusing**) a summary of the rules.

4. The team doctor ran onto the field toward the (**prone, solicitous**) figure of the injured football player.

5. The novelist is known for her (**staid, ornate**) writing style, using many unusual words, figures of speech, and involved constructions.

American poet Emily Dickinson wrote almost two thousand poems, but only about a dozen were published during her lifetime.

6. I think that talking loudly on the phone in public so that everyone knows about your private life is (**deplorable, blasé**) behavior.

7. When the mile run began, Ken quickly took the lead, but we knew that he could not (**sustain, obsess**) that pace for the entire race.

8. After the claims of all the creditors have been satisfied, the (**residue, qualms**) of the estate will be shared by the children.

9. My uncle is (**sustained, obsessed**) with football and spends all day Sunday watching every game on television.

10. I hope someday to build a house on that (**nonentity, promontory**) commanding a beautiful view of the bay.

11. Because they failed to deliver the goods on time, we felt justified in (**annulling, perusing**) the entire contract.

12. It is all very well to criticize and (**bolster, deplore**) the mistakes of young people, but why don't you also give them credit for their good qualities?

13. After months of rejection, Leah decided to hire a professional manager, hoping to (**peruse, bolster**) her acting career.

14. While my sister's memory is as retentive as a steel trap, mine seems to be as (**porous, blasé**) as a sieve.

15. The way the witness blushed and stuttered when questioned (**ousted, bolstered**) my suspicions that he was not telling the truth.

16. I would not call Lucy a friend, as she made no (**qualms, muster**) about sharing your secret with everyone!

17. My brother tried to appear (**blasé, obsessed**) when he was named to the honor society, but I know that he was thrilled.

18. I like jokes as much as anyone, but I don't approve of making such (**frivolous, porous**) remarks when a serious matter is under discussion.

19. We learned that behind the old professor's (**ornate, staid**) exterior there was a keen wit and a lively sense of what life is all about.

20. After being the apple of her eye for years, I suddenly found myself (**ousted, sustained**) from her affections by an upstart rival.

21. "It will take all the strength we can (**annul, muster**) to dislodge the enemy from that hill," the general observed grimly.

22. Only a person who is (**obsessed, bolstered**) with a desire to create beautiful music can become a great pianist or violinist.

23. That wonderful woman could not have been more (**solicitous, frivolous**) of me if she had been my own mother.

24. I believed at the time that I was justified in refusing to help them, but later I felt some (**qualms, recourse**) about it.

25. Those who think recess is a (**staid, frivolous**) activity do not see its purpose.

Synonyms

*Choose the word from this Unit that is the same or most nearly the same in meaning as the **boldface** word or expression in the phrase. Write that word on the line. Use a dictionary if necessary.*

1. to be regarded as an **unknown**   _____

2. **apt** to take unnecessary chances   _____

3. resisted efforts to **overthrow** the monarchy   _____

4. made of a **penetrable** material   _____

5. settled the dispute without **resort** to the law   _____

6. may **strengthen** your ability to resist colds   _____

7. chose an **intricate** silverware pattern   _____

8. scrubbed away the lime **deposit**   _____

9. special exercises to **maintain** muscle tone   _____

10. the spectacular view from the **headland**   _____

Antonyms

*Choose the word from this Unit that is most nearly opposite in meaning to the **boldface** word or expression in the phrase. Write that word on the line. Use a dictionary if necessary.*

1. the **entirety** of her mother's fortune _____

2. sheep grazing in the **lowlands** _____

3. an **unadorned** evening gown _____

4. designing a slick, **waterproof** fabric _____

5. a room crowded with **media superstars** _____

Completing the Sentence

From the words in this Unit, choose the one that best completes each of the following sentences. Write the correct word form in the space provided.

1. When we heard about our teacher's serious illness, we visited him daily in the hospital to _____ _____ his morale.

2. The furnishings in their house are so _____ that the place looks more like a museum than a family home.

3. It is now time for you to take your work seriously and to give up some of the _____ activities of your earlier years.

4. When we tried to carry water from the well, we found to our dismay that the bottom of the old bucket was _____.

5. Her public statements became so embarrassing that club members tried to _____ her from the presidency.

6. Every able-bodied citizen will be _____ into active military service to fight off the invading force.

7. "In that barren wasteland," the explorer said, "we had great difficulty finding enough food to _____ life."

8. When my cousin returned home after his first year in college, he tried to impress us with his sophisticated and _____ manner.

9. I do not criticize people for trying to get ahead, but I _____ any attempt to take unfair advantage of others.

10. There I was—an utter _____ in a group of famous and accomplished persons!

11. Some people seem to have no _____ about manipulating others to gain their own ends.

12. A lighthouse was built on the tip of the _____, where it served as a beacon for ships many miles away.

13. Because the villagers have so few dealings with the outside world, they are _____ to regard strangers with deep mistrust.

14. She is the kind of _____ teacher who aids and encourages her students in every way she can.

15. If you feel that you have been cheated, your only _____ is to make a complaint to the department of consumer affairs in your city.

16. People who constantly _____ about their weight may develop eating disorders.

17. Certain saltlike chemicals may effectively prevent the streets from icing up in winter, but the powdery _____ they leave behind can damage footwear.

18. I will not allow a single act of carelessness to _____ the results of years of hard work.

19. You should _____ the instructions with great care before you fill out your application for admission.

20. The two sisters are very different—one lively and fun-loving, the other quiet and rather _____.

Writing: Words in Action

1. Look back at "Toni Cade Bambara" (pages 50–51). Suppose you were going to write a story about social injustice. What would you write about? What would be the outcome of your story? Write a brief synopsis of your story, including its theme. Use at least two details from the passage and three Unit words.

2. *"Literature ... portrays an equally absorbing though better adjusted desire to know all kinds of life. The popular books are the novels, dealing with life under all possible conditions, and they are widely read not only because they are entertaining, but also because they in a measure satisfy an unformulated belief that to see farther, to know all sorts of men, in an indefinite way, is a preparation for better social adjustment—for the remedying of social ills."—Jane Addams*

Can literature help readers to understand different kinds of people? Can it serve as a "preparation...for the remedying of social ills"? In a brief essay, write about the social power of literature, and support your opinion with specific examples from the reading (pages 50–51), personal experience, or your studies. Write three paragraphs, and use three or more words from this Unit.

Vocabulary in Context

Literary Text

The following excerpts are from The Works of Edgar Allan Poe, *Volume 2 by Edgar Allan Poe. Some of the words you have studied in this Unit appear in **boldface** type. Complete each statement below the excerpt by circling the letter of the correct answer.*

1. Just opposite the **promontory** upon whose apex we were placed, and at a distance of some five or six miles out at sea, there was visible a small, bleak-looking island. . . . ("A Descent into the Maelström")

   A **promontory** is a(n)
   a. lake   **c.** bluff
   b. cavern   **d.** mountain

2. The grave was carelessly and loosely filled with an exceedingly **porous** soil; and thus some air was necessarily admitted. ("The Premature Burial")

   Soil that is **porous** is
   a. absorbent   **c.** rancid
   b. dense   **d.** arid

3. Another step before my fall, and the world had seen me no more. And the death just avoided, was of that very character which I had regarded as fabulous and **frivolous** in the tales respecting the Inquisition. ("The Pit and the Pendulum")

   Something regarded as **frivolous** is NOT
   a. minor   **c.** believable
   b. significant   **d.** exciting

An illustration from Poe's short story "The Pit and the Pendulum"

4. He was attired, as I had expected, in a costume altogether similar to my own; wearing a Spanish cloak of blue velvet, begirt about the waist with a crimson belt **sustaining** a rapier. A mask of black silk entirely covered his face. ("William Wilson")

   When something is **sustaining** another object, it is
   a. supporting it   **c.** decorating it
   b. complementing it   **d.** concealing it

5. To give to this a better coloring, I had contrived to have assembled a party of some eight or ten, and was **solicitously** careful that the introduction of cards should appear accidental, and originate in the proposal of my contemplated dupe himself. ("William Wilson")

   If an act is done **solicitously**, it is done with
   a. a lack of interest   **c.** clumsiness
   b. serious doubts   **d.** great care

Interactive Quiz

Snap the code, or go to **vocabularyworkshop.com**

*Read the following passage, taking note of the **boldface** words and their contexts. These words are among those you will be studying in Unit 5. As you complete the exercises in this Unit, it may help to refer to the way the words are used below.*

Reality Check
<Persuasive Essay>

Can we please write an **epitaph** for reality TV? It's been a controversial, even **volatile** issue since the very first reality shows appeared. Are the programs harmless escapism and fun, as their many fans claim? Or are they mean-spirited, vulgar displays that deserve our **disdain**? Some believe there is **ample** evidence that reality TV is contributing to the dumbing down of America.

Let's get real: Reality TV isn't going away any time soon, and reality programs, whether they're off-the-wall dramas or over-the-top competitions, are massive money makers that **pulverize** competing shows in the ratings. It's not **plausible** that TV executives will pull the plug on their cash cows.

But reality shows are proliferating at an alarming rate. More and more outrageous scenarios and crazy ideas—often aimed at the most **plebeian** tastes—are being given the green light. Standards are at an all-time low. Show directors create contrived situations—"Let's send the cast to Italy and unleash our 'heroes' on an unsuspecting populace!" or "Let's put a bunch of troubled people in **proximity** and see what happens!" Some programs are clearly **facetious** and light-hearted, but others leave us shaking our heads at the producers' **indiscriminate** lack of judgment, good taste, and values.

Meanwhile, reality shows that pit people against each other can be downright cruel. Participants are required to undergo

Reality show devotees argue that there's nothing wrong with giving people what they want. Others make the case that only snobs put down reality TV—and they can always change channels if they don't like what's on. But when more people tune in to watch a reality star get married than watch the nightly news, or when more people can name the cast of a reality show than can name their own state's senators, our society is in *big* trouble.

humiliating trials and perform risky stunts as they vie for cash and prizes. We watch contestants **cower** in fear as they confront writhing snakes, poisonous spiders, and other terrifying things. Or we cringe as they break down in tears in reaction to verbal abuse hurled at them by egotistical experts. Viewers are left wondering if the unprincipled show creators have an **ethical** bone in their bodies.

Just how real *are* these people and their adventures? Evidence indicates some shows are scripted, or at least mapped out ahead of time. It's pretty obvious that most are playing to the camera. Ordinary people become instant celebrities, but they're often exploited by the media and don't know how to handle their fame. The message is faulty: You don't have to work hard or be talented to achieve success; you just need to land on a reality show. It's not that easy—they're living in a fool's paradise.

As for "rehab" shows: Watching minor celebrities (or "D-listers") act out like toddlers and throw tantrums and scheme is like watching a train wreck in slo-mo— we can't turn away. There's **intrigue**! It's addictive! Just be sure to come back after the commercial break to see the next shocking and outlandish revelation!

We're experiencing reality overload, and it is time for a reality check. The Federal Communications Commission should **assert** its **jurisdiction** and put the brakes on the worst aspects of reality TV. Proponents of free speech might be **aghast**, but the national freak show needs to be tamed!

Audio

For iWords and audio passages, snap the code, or go to **vocabularyworkshop.com**.

Definitions

Note the spelling, pronunciation, part(s) of speech, and definition(s) of each of the following words. Then write the appropriate form of the word in the blank spaces in the illustrative sentence(s) following. Finally, study the lists of synonyms and antonyms.

1. addendum
(ə den' dəm)

(*n.*) a thing that is added; an appendix or addition to a book or written document

The woman amended her will with an _____ when her husband suddenly died.

SYNONYMS: attachment, rider, extension

2. aghast
(ə gast')

(*adj.*) filled with amazement, disgust, fear, or terror

People were _____ at the senseless brutality of the crime.

SYNONYMS: shocked, horrified, stupefied
ANTONYMS: delighted, overjoyed, unmoved

3. ample
(am' pəl)

(*adj.*) more than enough, large, spacious

Thanks to the wet spring weather, birds and other animals will have an _____ food supply for the rest of the year.

SYNONYMS: sufficient, adequate, considerable
ANTONYMS: insufficient, inadequate

4. apparition
(ap ə rish' ən)

(*n.*) a ghost or ghostly figure; an unexplained or unusual appearance

The vivid _____ seemed so real that it completely unnerved me.

SYNONYMS: phantom, specter

5. assert
(ə sərt')

(*v.*) to declare or state as truth, maintain or defend, put forward forcefully

Throughout the trial and the lengthy appeal process that followed, the defendant _____ her innocence.

SYNONYMS: affirm, avow

6. cower
(kaù' ər)

(*v.*) to crouch or shrink away in fear or shame

The kittens _____ in the corner, frightened by the huge, growling dog.

SYNONYMS: wince, flinch
ANTONYM: stand up to

7. disdain
(dis dān')

(*v.*) to look upon with scorn; to refuse scornfully; (*n.*) a feeling of contempt

I _____ their cowardly behavior.

Fair-minded people feel _____ for racism.

SYNONYMS: (*v.*) spurn, reject
ANTONYMS: (*v.*) revere, venerate, esteem, respect

8. epitaph
(ep' ə taf)

(*n.*) a brief statement written on a tomb or gravestone

Most people never stop to consider the words that might one day appear as their own _____.

SYNONYM: tombstone inscription

9. ethical
(eth' ə kəl)

(*adj.*) having to do with morals, values, right and wrong; in accordance with standards of right conduct; requiring a prescription for purchase

New developments in medicine often lead to discussions of important _____ questions.

SYNONYMS: upright, virtuous, honorable
ANTONYMS: immoral, unscrupulous, dishonest

10. facetious
(fə sē' shəs)

(*adj.*) humorous, not meant seriously

We had to laugh at her _____ remarks.

SYNONYMS: comical, witty, tongue-in cheek
ANTONYMS: serious, humorless

11. inaudible
(in ô' də bəl)

(*adj.*) not able to be heard

Some high-frequency sounds are _____ to even the keenest human ear.

SYNONYMS: faint, indistinct
ANTONYMS: audible, perceptible

12. indiscriminate
(in dis krim' ə nət)

(*adj.*) without restraint or control; unselective

The _____ slaughter of white whales brought that species to the brink of extinction.

SYNONYMS: haphazard, random, uncritical
ANTONYMS: selective, discriminating, judicious

13. intrigue
(*n.*, in' trēg;
v., in trēg')

(*n.*) crafty dealings, underhanded plotting; (*v.*) to form and carry out plots; to puzzle or excite the curiosity

Investigators uncovered a shocking network of lies and international _____.

The old album full of faded family pictures and postcards from exotic places _____ me.

SYNONYMS: (*n.*) scheme, plot, conspiracy
ANTONYM: (*n.*) fair play

14. jurisdiction
(jür is dik′ shən)

(n.) an area of authority or control; the right to administer justice
Cases involving robbery and assault are usually tried under the _____ of the state courts.

SYNONYMS: purview, supervision

15. plausible
(plô′ zə bəl)

(adj.) appearing true, reasonable, or fair
Their story didn't sound _____ to me.

SYNONYMS: believable, probable
ANTONYMS: improbable, unbelievable, unlikely

16. plebeian
(plə bē′ ən)

(adj.) common, vulgar; belonging to the lower class; (n.) a common person, member of the lower class

The couple's taste in cars is quite _____.

At one time, the _____ of ancient Rome were excluded from holding public office of any kind.

SYNONYMS: (adj.) lowborn, proletarian, coarse, unrefined
ANTONYMS: (adj.) aristocratic, refined, cultivated

17. prodigal
(präd′ ə gəl)

(adj.) wastefully extravagant; lavishly or generously abundant; (n.) one who is wasteful and self-indulgent

We have a tight budget, but we make an exception for _____ celebrations of family birthdays.

The elderly man told us that he greatly regretted the years he spent living the life of a _____.

SYNONYMS: (adj.) improvident; (n.) spendthrift, wastrel
ANTONYMS: (adj.) frugal, economical, stingy, miserly

18. proximity
(präk sim′ ə tē)

(n.) nearness, closeness
The house's _____ to schools is an asset.

ANTONYMS: distance, remoteness

19. pulverize
(pəl′ və rīz)

(v.) to grind or pound to a powder or dust; to destroy or overcome (as though by smashing into fragments)

At many old mills in Vermont, granite stones were used to _____ the grain.

SYNONYMS: compress, demolish

20. volatile
(väl′ ə təl)

(adj.) highly changeable, fickle; tending to become violent or explosive; changing readily from the liquid to the gaseous state

A person who is usually calm and collected may nevertheless sometimes behave in a _____ manner.

SYNONYMS: unstable, erratic
ANTONYMS: stable, steady, static, inert, dormant

Choosing the Right Word

*Select the **boldface** word that better completes each sentence. You might refer to the passage on pages 60–61 to see how most of these words are used in context.*

1. I wonder how many asteroids Superman could (**disdain, pulverize**) with his bare hands.

2. You can show respect for your supervisors without seeming to (**assert, cower**) whenever one of them speaks to you.

3. Deciding who is or isn't eligible for school athletic teams is not within the (**proximity, jurisdiction**) of the student council.

4. The purpose of this experiment is to find out whether a substance will dissolve more rapidly in water if it is thoroughly (**cowered, pulverized**).

5. Although I may not agree with what you have to say, I will always (**assert, disdain**) your right to say it.

6. Your thoughtless remarks hurt me deeply, even though you say that you were merely trying to be (**plausible, facetious**).

Superman's first appearance was in Action Comics No. 1 from 1938.

7. In recent decades, we have been forced to make greater use of our (**ample, inaudible**) coal supply to meet our growing energy needs.

8. It takes a practiced eye to make out the (**epitaphs, addendums**) on old, weather-beaten tombstones in a country churchyard.

9. One of the most (**intriguing, prodigal**) mysteries I have ever read involved a priest and was set in the Wild West.

10. I do not believe that people who come from poor families should be regarded as (**apparitions, plebeians**).

11. Government officials believe the pirate situation occurring in the high seas remains (**inaudible, volatile**) and requires immediate action.

12. My neighbor's furniture is supposed to be "original" and "colorful," but I think it is a(n) (**indiscriminate, facetious**) collection of junk.

13. It will take the two of us months of strict economizing to make up for this one weekend of (**ethical, prodigal**) shopping.

14. In Shakespeare's *Macbeth*, the witches show the title character three prophetic (**ethics, apparitions**).

15. I find my friend's stories about life in her native country most (**plebeian, intriguing**).

16. Only a snob would show such (**disdain, intrigue**) for someone who doesn't drive a fancy car.

17. The tenant wanted the landlord to include a mold (**apparition, addendum**) in his lease so the owner would be responsible for any mold problems.

18. The (**proximity, epitaph**) of the leaders' ideas on many subjects made it easy for them to work together during that critical period of our history.

19. Sometimes, it is difficult to tell if my brother is being (**facetious, ethical**) or if he really means the things he says.

20. The voters, (**volatile, aghast**) that such scandal could occur in their town, demanded the mayor's immediate resignation.

21. I thought that my whispers to you were (**prodigal, inaudible**), but I learned otherwise when the teacher told me in no uncertain terms to be quiet.

22. Her moods are so (**ample, volatile**) that we never know if she will be in a good humor or down in the dumps.

23. His explanation that he is failing math because "the teacher is down on me" doesn't seem (**plausible, volatile**).

24. Lawyers may be punished by disbarment if it can be shown that they have violated the (**ethics, epitaphs**) of the legal profession.

25. The (**apparition, proximity**) of nuclear war inspired the international agreement.

Synonyms

*Choose the word from this Unit that is the same or most nearly the same in meaning as the **boldface** word or expression in the phrase. Write that word on the line. Use a dictionary if necessary.*

1. a function that makes the television **muted** _____

2. **crushed** turquoise to use as paint pigment _____

3. under the **authorization** of the United Nations _____

4. a letter that includes a **postscript** _____

5. **mystified** by their unusual behavior _____

6. refused to help the **squanderer** _____

7. known for having a highly **unpredictable** disposition _____

8. the clearest way to **pronounce** our freedom _____

9. **cringed** as the tornado roared past _____

10. terrified by **spirits** _____

Antonyms

*Choose the word from this Unit that is most nearly opposite in meaning to the **boldface** word or expression in the phrase. Write that word on the line. Use a dictionary if necessary.*

1. a person with **thrifty** spending habits _____

2. pointed out an **omission** in the contract _____

3. made a reply that was **easily heard** _____

4. offered us a **far-fetched** alibi _____

5. visited by a **corporeal being** _____

Completing the Sentence

From the words in this Unit, choose the one that best completes each of the following sentences. Write the correct word form in the space provided.

1. The giant crushers lifted the boulders and quickly _____ them into a uniform gray powder.

2. The way the child _____ around Rex gave me the impression that he had a fear of dogs.

3. The planning board refused to allow the construction of a factory in close _____ to our school building.

4. People of all religions strive to live up to high moral and _____ standards.

5. In that elegant French restaurant, which serves all kinds of fancy foods, she ordered a(n) _____ ham and cheese on rye.

6. I appreciate your _____ display of gratitude, but a simple "thank you" would do.

7. Did Ben Jonson write the _____ engraved on Shakespeare's tombstone?

8. For the moment the crowd was quiet and subdued, but we knew that it was so _____ that it might become ugly and dangerous at any time.

9. I hope he was just being _____ when he said that my dancing reminded him of a trained bear.

10. Although they did not dare to attack the emperor publicly, they _____ in secret to bring about his downfall.

11. Since you were given _____ time to prepare your report, I can see no excuse for your failure to complete it.

12. A(n) _____ TV viewer, who watches any program, good or bad, is bound to waste a lot of time.

13. Observers on the ground were _____ to see the rocket explode and plunge back to earth seconds after launch.

14. The writer of the mystery story set up an interesting situation, but in my opinion the ending was not _____.

15. Regulation of radio and TV stations falls within the _____ of the federal government.

16. The "ghostly figure" you think you saw in the graveyard was no more than a(n) _____ created by your imagination.

17. Who would be so proud or so foolish as to _____ a helping hand in time of real need?

18. Because the P.A. system was not working, the voice of the speaker was completely _____ to most of the people in the hall.

19. In answer to unfair criticisms, we proudly _____ that our family has always been generous in its aid to the needy.

20. Notes from a rare interview were included as a(n) _____ in the second edition of the comedian's biography.

Writing: Words in Action

1. Look back at "Reality Check" (pages 60–61). Suppose you are a TV executive. Your network has been receiving many complaints and criticisms about a particular reality show, but the show's ratings are good. The show is also inexpensive to produce. However, many critics and viewers say that the program is in bad taste and reflects poorly on the network. You must decide whether to keep televising the reality show or to replace it with new programming that might be more expensive to produce. Write an argument using at least two details from the passage and three Unit words to support your position.

2. The writer of "Reality Check" (pages 60–61) states that "when more people can name the cast of a reality show than can name their own state's senators, our society is in *big* trouble." Do you agree with this viewpoint? In a brief essay, support your opinion with evidence and examples from your studies, the reading (refer to pages 60–61), or personal experience. Write at least three paragraphs, and use three or more words from this Unit.

Vocabulary in Context

The following excerpts are from A Christmas Carol *by Charles Dickens. Some of the words you have studied in this Unit appear in* **boldface** *type. Complete each statement below the excerpt by circling the letter of the correct answer.*

1. The **apparition** walked backward from him; and at every step it took, the window raised itself a little, so that when the specter reached it, it was wide open.

    An **apparition** is a

  a. celebrity   **c.** phantom
  b. diplomat   **d.** tenant

2. "I am the Ghost of Christmas Present," said the Spirit. "Look upon me!"

Scrooge reverently did so. It was clothed in one simple green robe, or mantle, bordered with white fur. This garment hung so loosely on the figure, that its capacious breast was bare, as if **disdaining** to be warded or concealed by any artifice.

    The act of **disdaining** involves

  a. reverence   **c.** speculation
  b. rejection   **d.** deliberation

Reginald Owen plays Ebenezer Scrooge in this 1938 film adaptation of *A Christmas Carol.*

3. Its feet, observable beneath the **ample** folds of the garment, were also bare; and on its head it wore no other covering than a holly wreath, set here and there with shining icicles.

    If an item of clothing has **ample** folds, the folds are

  a. uncommon   **c.** burdensome
  b. appealing   **d.** abundant

4. Uncle Scrooge had imperceptibly become so. . . light of heart, that he would have pledged the unconscious company in return, and thanked them in an **inaudible** speech, if the Ghost had given him time.

    Speech that is **inaudible** is

  a. hushed   **c.** enthusiastic
  b. distinct   **d.** deafening

5. Scrooge resumed his labors with an improved opinion of himself, and in a more **facetious** temper than was usual with him.

    Someone who is **facetious** is NOT

  a. teasing   **c.** somber
  b. honest   **d.** flippant

Interactive Quiz

Snap the code, or go to **vocabularyworkshop.com**

Read the following passage, taking note of the **boldface** words and their contexts. These words are among those you will be studying in Unit 6. As you complete the exercises in this Unit, it may help to refer to the way the words are used below.

Diary of a Young Migrant Worker
<Diary Entry>

All the children worked, here as cotton laborers in Arizona, 1937.

This is a fictional diary of 12-year-old Eldora Soto Vega, a Mexican American girl in a family of migrant farmworkers in California in 1940. The family lived in temporary camps and moved from farm to farm to follow seasonal work, picking crops.

September 15, 1940

We are now on an enormous farm in the San Joaquin Valley, picking cotton. My brother Emilio is back after picking grapes in Napa. The long, hot days in the fields picking avocados and cantaloupes made us tired, because we started at five in the morning! The Anglos **ostracize** *campesinos*, and we stay in our own camps, sometimes living near an irrigation ditch. We use the ditch water for all our needs, and Mamá said this is why many get sick. The other farmworkers don't live like kings, but at least their camps have toilets and running water.

October 5, 1940

A few of the Anglo kids around here are nice, but most are **aloof** and ignore us, and some are just plain mean. I am jealous of a girl who **flaunts** her new jacket, **basking** in compliments, while my shoes are two sizes too small. My mother called California "the Land of Milk and Honey," but I am more **forthright**: How can such a bountiful place be so cruel?

People worked long hours under the hot sun for little pay.

Some families were lucky enough to have their own car. Here, stranded migrants in 1936 California wait for help.

We are **scapegoats** when anything goes wrong—like yesterday, one of the bushels of cotton went missing. The foreman blamed my father, but we all know it was the foreman's nephew who misplaced it.

November 8, 1940

We are camped at another farm 20 miles north, picking peas. The rain is leaking through our shack's roof of burlap and palm leaves and onto my diary. It's one of the many **defects** of our little dwelling, but at least the rain gives us a chance to rest. My name, Eldora, means "golden," and Papá said he wanted to **instill** pride in me by giving me a name with significance. I try to remember that when I see signs like this one at the park: "For White People Only. Mexicans and Filipinos Keep Out."

December 1, 1940

Our **genial** neighbor, Señora Medina, has set up a *taqueria* for the workers. She is getting a little old for fieldwork, but she wants to help the community, for in time of test, family is best. There was only enough corn dough for one taco each, and I am **abashed** to admit I took a second one. Señor Medina caught me, and I'm scared of **repercussions**, so I'll hide until things blow over!

December 6, 1940

I heard Mamá telling Papá she had a **premonition** something terrible would happen, and she was right. Our old car broke down, and now it's propped up on bricks because Papá sold the tires. Mamá tries to hide her **anguish,** but she is worried, because we can be "repatriated" to Mexico at any time, especially if we can no longer get from place to place. We were all born here, but we have no papers to prove it, and many others have already been sent back in a **purge** of Mexican and Mexican American workers. Officials say they want to keep the few jobs for "real" Americans. That's why Papá won't join a strike, even though he agrees with the strikers, because he can't risk being arrested.

December 20, 1940

Everyone says to stop dreaming, but I am **resolute**—when I am grown, I will have a little house, and it will be more than a shack made out of cardboard boxes. I will have a garden, too. And I will go to school, and my children will not have to work like my brothers and sisters and I must.

Audio

For iWords and audio passages, snap the code, or go to **vocabularyworkshop.com**.

Definitions

Note the spelling, pronunciation, part(s) of speech, and definition(s) of each of the following words. Then write the appropriate form of the word in the blank spaces in the illustrative sentence(s) following. Finally, study the lists of synonyms and antonyms.

1. abashed
(ə basht')

(*adj.*, *part.*) embarrassed, ashamed, or nonplussed

I was thoroughly _____ by the foolish mistake I made at the dinner party.

ANTONYMS: unembarrassed, unashamed

2. aloof
(ə lüf')

(*adj.*) withdrawn, standing apart from others by choice

In almost every office or business, there are some people who keep decidedly _____ from their coworkers.

SYNONYMS: distant, cold; ANTONYMS: involved, sociable

3. anguish
(aŋ' gwish)

(*n.*) great mental suffering, distress, or pain; (*v.*) to cause deep pain or sorrow

Survivors of a natural disaster often suffer great mental _____ long after their terrible ordeal is over.

The child's disappearance _____ every member of the community.

SYNONYMS: (*n.*) misery, woe, torment
ANTONYMS: (*n.*) joy, delight, peace of mind

4. articulate
(*v.*, är tik' yü lāt;
adj., är tik' yə lit)

(*v.*) to pronounce distinctly; to express well in words; to fit together into a system; (*adj.*) able to use language effectively; expressed clearly and forcefully

A successful candidate can _____ ideas in a way that makes them acceptable to voters.

To be successful as a professional lecturer, a person must, of necessity, be _____.

SYNONYMS: (*v.*) expound; (*adj.*) eloquent
ANTONYMS: (*adj.*) tongue-tied, mumbled

5. bask
(bask)

(*v.*) to be in, or expose oneself to, pleasant warmth; to take pleasure in or derive enjoyment from

Because they are cold-blooded, lizards and other reptiles must _____ in the sun to regulate their body temperature.

SYNONYMS: wallow, revel

6. defect
(*n.*, dē' fekt;
v., di fekt')

(*n.*) an imperfection, flaw, or blemish of some kind; (*v.*) to desert a cause or organization

There is no one who does not have at least one serious character _____.

In 1948 the Dixiecrats, a group of Southern Democrats, _____ from the Democratic Party and held their own presidential nominating convention.

7. finesse
(fi nes')

(*n.*) delicate skill; tact and cleverness; (*v.*) to accomplish something by cleverness, good judgment, or skillful evasion

To become a champion, a tennis player needs to combine power with _____.

Skilled politicians know how to _____ their answers to embarrassing questions from reporters.

SYNONYMS: (*n.*) delicacy, subtlety
ANTONYMS: (*n.*) clumsiness, awkwardness

8. flaunt
(flônt)

(*v.*) to wave or flutter showily; to display in a conceited, offensive way

Some people seem to need to _____ their wealth and good fortune in life.

SYNONYMS: show off, parade; ANTONYMS: hide, downplay

9. forthright
(fôrth' rīt)

(*adj.*) frank, direct, straightforward

I appreciate the _____ way in which you express your opinions, even when they do not agree with my own.

SYNONYMS: candid, blunt
ANTONYMS: indirect, evasive, deceitful, two-faced

10. genial
(jēn' yəl)

(*adj.*) cordial, pleasantly cheerful or warm

The _____ host and hostess made each party guest feel especially welcome.

SYNONYMS: friendly, amiable
ANTONYMS: cold, unfriendly, unsociable

11. instill
(in stil')

(*v.*) to add gradually; to introduce or cause to be taken in

How can parents best _____ in their children a love for reading?

SYNONYMS: implant, infuse, inculcate
ANTONYMS: root out, eradicate, extirpate

12. ostracize
(äs' trə sīz)

(*v.*) to exclude from a group, banish, send away

Society _____ those who commit acts of treason.

SYNONYMS: cast out, expel, blackball
ANTONYMS: fraternize with, associate with

13. premonition
(prē mə nish′ ən)

(*n.*) forewarning or foreboding of a future event

I felt a vague _____ of danger as I entered the abandoned building.

SYNONYM: presentiment

14. pseudonym
(sü′ də nim)

(*n.*) a pen name, name assumed by a writer

It is wise to use a _____ to protect your privacy when you chat on the Internet.

SYNONYM: nom de plume

15. purge
(pərj)

(*v.*) to wash away impurities, clean up; (*n.*) the process of getting rid of something or someone decisively

A soaking rainstorm will usually _____ the air of pollutants.

The change of government was achieved through an election, not through a brutal _____ .

SYNONYMS: (*v.*) cleanse, purify
ANTONYMS: (*v.*) pollute, contaminate, defile

16. rehabilitate
(rē hə bil′ ə tāt)

(*v.*) to make over in good form; to restore to good condition or to a former position

Government agencies have spent sums of money trying to _____ run-down inner-city neighborhoods.

SYNONYMS: reclaim, rebuild, reform

17. repercussion
(rē pər kəsh′ ən)

(*n.*) an effect or consequence of some action or event, result; an echo or reverberation

The _____ of the 1929 stock market crash were felt all over the world.

ANTONYMS: cause, source

18. resolute
(rez′ ə lüt)

(*adj.*) bold, determined; firm

Commencement-day speakers generally urge graduates to be _____ in pursuit of their dreams.

SYNONYMS: steadfast, unflinching; ANTONYMS: weak, spineless

19. retentive
(ri tent′ iv)

(*adj.*) able to hold, keep, or recall; retaining knowledge easily

A _____ memory is a great asset for any actor.

ANTONYMS: porous, forgetful

20. scapegoat
(skāp′ gōt)

(*n.*) a person or thing carrying the blame for others

In ancient times, a messenger who brought bad news was often made the _____ for it and killed.

SYNONYM: whipping boy

Choosing the Right Word

Select the **boldface** word that better completes each sentence. You might refer to the passage on pages 70–71 to see how most of these words are used in context.

1. Many female authors once used male (**repercussions, pseudonyms**) because it was considered improper for women to write novels.

2. She has lived (**aloof, retentive**) from other people for so long that it is hard for her to take part in everyday social affairs.

3. He's cleverly managed to (**rehabilitate, finesse**) his way into a very important position in this company.

4. It will be better if we all take responsibility for the mistake instead of letting one employee be the (**pseudonym, scapegoat**).

Emily Brontë wrote under the pen name Ellis Bell.

5. His prejudices are so strong that he wants to (**ostracize, bask**) all members of minority religious groups.

6. Jefferson preferred to (**articulate, defect**) his ideas about government and religion in writing rather than give public speeches.

7. Although he was trying to look unconcerned, I could see that he was much (**abashed, aloof**) by the teacher's criticism.

8. An actor who has (**basked, instilled**) for so long in the favor of the public finds it hard to realize that he or she is no longer popular.

9. It was shocking how quickly the singer was (**ostracized, defected**) for voicing her opinions about free speech.

10. She is not the most (**forthright, genial**) person in the world, but in her own way she is at least trying to be friendly.

11. The new governor's address was an unusually (**articulate, abashed**) and effective description of the challenges facing the state in the years ahead.

12. No matter how much time or effort it takes, I will (**purge, instill**) these unfair charges of disloyalty from my reputation!

13. Is it our duty to try to (**ostracize, instill**) a faith in democracy in the people of other lands?

14. My (**anguish, finesse**) at the loss of a loved one was all the greater when I realized that my carelessness had caused the accident.

15. The college student did not understand the serious (**premonitions, repercussions**) of plagiarism when he downloaded an essay from the Internet.

16. How can we ever forgive him for (**defecting, purging**) from our great cause at the very time we needed him most?

17. Fortunately, the soil is so (**resolute, retentive**) of moisture that the weeks of dry weather did not damage our crops.

18. By teaching her son how to garden and fish, Hilary hoped to (**flaunt, instill**) in him a love of nature.

19. I did not think that such an innocent conversation could have such serious (**repercussions, scapegoats**) on the outcome of an election.

20. It is possible to be honest and (**forthright, retentive**) in stating your views and opinions without being cruel or tactless.

21. Shakespeare tries to convey Brutus's (**defects, premonitions**) of defeat at Philippi by having Caesar's ghost appear to him the night before the battle.

22. We should now be just as (**genial, resolute**) in fighting for peace as the Americans of two hundred years ago were in fighting for independence.

23. It would be good taste on his part not to (**flaunt, ostracize**) all the honors and awards that he has won.

24. The purpose of our prison system is not just to punish offenders but to (**flaunt, rehabilitate**) them.

25. Many people view cats as (**finesse, aloof**) and averse to cuddling.

Synonyms

*Choose the word from this Unit that is the same or most nearly the same in meaning as the **boldface** word or expression in the phrase. Write that word on the line. Use a dictionary if necessary.*

1. needs to **enunciate** words more clearly _____

2. **snubbed** the newcomers _____

3. a **watertight** vessel _____

4. **ingrain** in them a love of country _____

5. **restores** antique cars as a hobby _____

6. refuse to be made the **fall guy** again _____

7. **expel** the vermin from the house _____

8. accepting praise with **poise** _____

9. a rather **standoffish** disposition _____

10. used an **assumed name** to conceal my identity _____

Antonyms

*Choose the word from this Unit that is most nearly opposite in meaning to the **boldface** word or expression in the phrase. Write that word on the line. Use a dictionary if necessary.*

1. **demolish** an old shopping center _____

2. signed the book with his **real name** _____

3. used a **permeable** plant container _____

4. handled the matter with surprising **inelegance** _____

5. gave an **incoherent** statement to reporters _____

Completing the Sentence

From the words in this Unit, choose the one that best completes each of the following sentences. Write the correct word form in the space provided.

1. We learned that beneath the old man's quiet and withdrawn manner, there was a charming and _____ personality.

2. The star basketball player _____ in the admiration of every small child in the neighborhood.

3. Since we all know that you sing and play the piano beautifully, what need is there for you to _____ your musical talents?

4. By the example of their own conduct, our parents _____ in us a deep respect for people of all races, nationalities, and religions.

5. The city planner said that in addition to building new housing, we should plan to _____ many old buildings.

6. Although every form of government has its _____, democracy has more pluses and fewer minuses than any other.

7. The speaker could not be understood easily because he swallowed his words instead of _____ them clearly.

8. I criticize him not because he makes mistakes but because he constantly looks for a(n) _____ to take the blame for them.

9. It took four years of civil war to _____ this nation of the curse of slavery.

10. The defendant was found not guilty at his trial, but his punishment came when he was _____ by all his friends.

11. Instead of a(n) _____ answer, all we got from her was, "In one sense, yes, but on the other hand, perhaps no."

12. Even though I assured my friend that I would visit him when he moved abroad, I had a strange _____ that I would never see him again.

13. Good citizens don't remain _____ from the problems and troubles in their communities.

14. I have learned over the years that it is often possible to accomplish more by _____ than by brute force.

15. She has such a(n) _____ mind that she seems able to master complicated details without even taking notes.

16. I think you will know who William S. Porter was if I tell you that he used the _____ O. Henry.

17. Our _____ turned to joy when the missing plane and its passengers landed safely.

18. After the infamous attack on Pearl Harbor, the American people were _____ in their determination to defeat the fascist powers.

19. Although Hal was the only boy at the formal dance wearing sneakers and an old sweatshirt, he did not seem at all _____.

20. In recent years, pollution of our waterways has had serious and sometimes fatal _____ on the wildlife that inhabits them.

Writing: Words in Action

1. Look back at "Diary of a Young Migrant Worker" (pages 70–71). How does your life differ from that of Eldora? Write a brief essay in which you compare and contrast your life with that of the young migrant worker. Use at least two details from the passage and three Unit words.

2. What is the American Dream? How can it be attained? Is it achievable for all? Why or why not? In a brief essay, respond to these questions. Support your view with details and examples from your studies, the reading (refer to pages 70–71), or personal experience. Write at least three paragraphs, and use three or more words from this Unit.

Vocabulary in Context

The following excerpts are from The Call of the Wild *and* White Fang *by Jack London. Some of the words you have studied in this Unit appear in* **boldface** *type. Complete each statement below the excerpt by circling the letter of the correct answer.*

1. . . . this song of the huskies might have been the defiance of life, only it was pitched in minor key, with long-drawn wailings and half-sobs, and was more the pleading of life, the **articulate** travail of existence. (*The Call of the Wild*)

   If something is **articulate**, it is

   a. emotionless   c. expressive
   b. defined   d. pondered

2. "Well, Buck, my boy," he went on in a **genial** voice, "we've had our little ruction, and the best thing we can do is to let it go at that. You've learned your place, and I know mine." (*The Call of the Wild*)

   A **genial** voice is NOT

   a. good-natured   c. hoarse
   b. hostile   d. friendly

3. It was because nothing daunted him that he had been chosen for government courier. He took all manner of risks, **resolutely** thrusting his little weazened face into the frost and struggling on from dim dawn to dark. (*The Call of the Wild*)

   If a person proceeds **resolutely**, he or she does so with

   a. indifference   c. experience
   b. cleverness   d. determination

In this film adaptation of *The Call of the Wild*, Clark Gable playo Jack Thornton.

4. The noise from downstairs was as that of a score of battling fiends. There were revolver shots. A man's voice screamed once in horror and **anguish**. There was a great snarling and growling, and over all arose a smashing and crashing of furniture and glass. (*White Fang*)

   If a person screams in **anguish,** he or she is experiencing

   a. agony   c. depression
   b. regret   d. isolation

5. But it can scarcely be said that White Fang was a member of the gang. He did not mingle with it, but remained **aloof**, always himself, and was even feared by it. (*White Fang*)

   If an animal is **aloof**, he is

   a. playful   c. outgoing
   b. reserved   d. strong

Interactive Quiz

Snap the code, or go to **vocabularyworkshop.com**

Vocabulary for Comprehension

*Read the following passage in which some of the words you have studied in Units 4–6 appear in **boldface** type. Then answer the questions on page 81.*

When—and why—did people start to use umbrellas? The answers given in this passage may surprise you.

(Line)

Most people probably take the umbrella for granted. Almost everyone has one. But there was a time when the umbrella was a rare

(5) possession reserved for royalty.

Umbrellas were first used for protection from the sun. In fact, the word *umbrella* comes from the Latin *umbra*, which means "shade." The

(10) umbrella made shade portable.

The earliest known depiction of an umbrella appears on a monument to a Mesopotamian king, Sargon of Akkad, that dates from about

(15) 2400 B.C. The king is shown leading his victorious army while a **solicitous** aide walks behind him, shading him with an umbrella. Umbrellas also appear in the art of

(20) ancient Egypt, Greece, India, Rome, and China. Everywhere, the umbrella was associated with the elite, not with **plebeians**.

Umbrellas made of paper were

(25) **porous** and therefore of little use as protection in stormy weather. During the Wei dynasty (A.D. 386–535), the Chinese devised an oiled-paper umbrella for use in sun or rain. The

(30) emperor's **ornate** umbrella was red and yellow, the royal colors. The ancient Romans also developed oiled-paper umbrellas. In the fourteenth century, weavers

(35) fashioned silk fabrics sturdy enough to use for umbrellas.

In 1340, a papal envoy to India wrote of a "little tent-roof on a cane handle," which the people "open out

(40) at will as a protection against sun or rain." The envoy brought an umbrella back to Italy. However, the device was slow to gain popularity in Europe, where it was considered a

(45) woman's accessory. Men would have been embarrassed to be seen using an umbrella, even in the heaviest downpour.

The umbrella did not catch on with

(50) men until around 1750, when a British gentleman named Jonas Hanway began carrying one almost every day. He **sustained** years of public ridicule for doing so. But

(55) eventually Hanway convinced people that carrying an umbrella in rainy London was both stylish and practical. Thanks to his persistence, it became acceptable for everyone

(60) to use the umbrella.

1. The main purpose of the passage is to
   a. inform readers about the history of umbrellas
   b. explain the etymology of the word *umbrella*
   c. entertain readers with fictional details about umbrellas
   d. persuade readers to use umbrellas as protection from the sun's rays
   e. examine how the design of umbrellas has changed over the centuries

2. The passage is organized in
   a. spatial order
   b. cause–effect order
   c. chronological order
   d. comparison–contrast order
   e. order of importance

3. The meaning of **solicitous** (line 17) is
   a. tired
   b. smiling
   c. faithful
   d. frightened
   e. concerned

4. **Plebeians** (line 23) most nearly means
   a. athletes
   b. professionals
   c. aristocrats
   d. common people
   e. royalty

5. In paragraph 3 (lines 11–23), you learn that the earliest known use of umbrellas has been dated at 2400 B.C. from evidence given
   a. on a monument
   b. in a photograph
   c. in a traveler's journal
   d. in a historical document
   e. in an eyewitness account

6. **Porous** (line 25) is best defined as
   a. fragile
   b. durable
   c. colorful
   d. permeable
   e. decorative

7. The meaning of **ornate** (line 30) is
   a. ample
   b. simple
   c. elaborate
   d. ordinary
   e. elegant

8. **Sustained** (line 53) is best defined as
   a. attracted
   b. ignored
   c. nourished
   d. welcomed
   e. suffered

9. The tone of this passage can best be described as
   a. ironic
   b. factual
   c. critical
   d. skeptical
   e. humorous

10. Which of the following best states Jonas Hanway's contribution?
    a. He made the umbrella acceptable to men.
    b. He improved the umbrella's design.
    c. He made umbrellas popular in Europe.
    d. He made waterproof umbrellas.
    e. He popularized the umbrella among the common people.

11. Jonas Hanway is best described as
    a. crafty
    b. sorrowful
    c. practical
    d. aggressive
    e. foolish

12. Which generalization would the author agree with?
    a. Umbrellas were invented in Italy.
    b. Umbrellas were immediately popular with both women and men.
    c. In ancient times, umbrellas were used only by the common people.
    d. Umbrellas were in common use in Asia before they were used in Europe.
    e. Umbrellas were first used as protection from rain

Two-Word Completions

Select the pair of words that best completes the meaning of each of the following sentences.

1. Since her objections to the plan were clearly _____, I thought that she was being _____. After all, if she had been serious, her comments would have had more substance.
   a. plausible . . . articulate
   b. genial . . . solicitous
   c. inaudible . . . forthright
   d. frivolous . . . facetious

2. Some of my friends have remarkably _____ memories from which nothing ever seems to escape. Unfortunately, I've been blessed with a memory that is as _____ as a sieve.
   a. staid . . . durable
   b. retentive . . . porous
   c. ample . . . volatile
   d. devoid . . . prodigious

3. Elected officials cannot be too careful about their behavior while in office. If they become _____ about matters of right and wrong, they may do things that the average citizen of this country does not consider _____. Such mistakes could cost the offenders their jobs.
   a. solicitous . . . plausible
   b. obsessed . . . prodigal
   c. blasé . . . ethical
   d. resolute . . . indiscriminate

4. During the bloody _____ of the early 1930s, Joseph Stalin "liquidated" every potential rival whom he feared might one day seek to _____ him from his position as absolute master.
   a. purges . . . oust
   b. repercussions . . . sustain
   c. premonitions . . . ostracize
   d. jurisdictions . . . intrigue

5. Though I tried to _____ my words clearly and distinctly, the roar of the storm caused my voice to be almost _____ .
   a. sustain . . . ample
   b. bolster . . . abashed
   c. articulate . . . inaudible
   d. muster . . . prone

6. "Using a(n) _____ has caused me a really unexpected problem," the famous novelist remarked. "Most people only know me by my pen name. So if I introduce myself by my real name, I run the risk of being regarded as a complete _____."
   a. pseudonym . . . nonentity
   b. bolster . . . scapegoat
   c. addendum . . . plebeian
   d. epitaph . . . apparition

7. "His cold and distant attitude toward people clearly betrays his deep _____ for the human race," I observed. "No one who genuinely likes human beings would constantly prefer to remain so _____ from them."
   a. apparition . . . solicitous
   b. disdain . . . aloof
   c. anguish . . . prone
   d. obsession . . . abashed

Idioms

In the passage about Toni Cade Bambara (see pages 50–51), the narrator describes one of Bambara's characters, Squeaky. The narrator states that although Squeaky enjoyed a wealth of wisdom, she was not born on "Easy Street." What the narrator means is that Squeaky's life was not an easy one.

"Easy Street" is an idiom that refers to a life of comfort or material wealth. An **idiom** is an everyday expression that should be understood figuratively, not literally. Some idioms are particular to a certain region or culture, while others are used more universally. Every language has its own idioms.

Choosing the Right Idiom

Read each sentence. Use context clues to figure out the meaning of each idiom in **boldface** *print. Then write the letter of the definition for the idiom in the sentence.*

1. When confronted with electrical and plumbing problems, Benny realized he was **in over his head** with the kitchen remodel. _____

2. I would really like to help you, but **my hands are tied** and there is nothing I can do. _____

3. Glenn wants to run for mayor, but many think he's still **wet behind the ears** _____

4. "Don't worry about losing your job; I've **got your back**," Liam said. _____

5. When the rest of the clean-up crew left without notice, Jill was **left holding the bag**. _____

6. Lori volunteered for everything this summer, and I fear she **spread herself too thin**. _____

7. If you haven't heard the news, you must be **living under a rock**. _____

8. My grandpa likes to spend time at the coffee shop **chewing the fat** with the neighbors. _____

9. The Wilsons needed more **elbow room** and so moved into a bigger home. _____

10. Only a driver with **eagle eyes** can find a parking space at the mall during the holidays. _____

a. be unaware of what's going on in the world

b. adequate space to move about

c. keen vision

d. unable to act due to restrictions

e. having casual conversation

f. young and inexperienced

g. took on too many obligations

h. challenged by a task beyond one's ability or means

i. left to complete something that was another person's responsibility

j. looking out for someone's welfare; supporting a friend

Writing with Idioms

Find the meaning of each idiom. (Use a dictionary if necessary.) Then write a sentence for each idiom.

1. pick someone's brain

_____

2. hit rock bottom

_____

3. two left feet

_____

4. starry eyed

_____

5. counting sheep

_____

_____

6. boiling point

_____

_____

7. a lone wolf

_____

_____

8. bursting at the seams

_____

9. speak with a forked tongue

_____

10. eat humble pie

_____

11. on the dot

_____

12. hold the fort

_____

Denotation and Connotation

When you use a dictionary to find a word's definition, you learn the word's **denotation**, or its literal meaning. A word's denotation is its "surface" meaning, and it is generally neutral.

Many words also have connotations. A **connotation** is a word's emotional charge, the meaning that resides "under the surface." Connotations, or implied meanings, build up around words over time. Connotations can be positive or negative. We may associate certain words with positive feelings, yet assign negative meanings to other words that share a similar denotation.

Consider these synonyms for the neutral word *press*.

> *grind   crush   pulverize   demolish*

Grind and *crush* describe less powerful actions than *pulverize* and *demolish*, which are stronger words with more negative connotations.

> **Think:** You might grind or crush a handful of nuts to use in a recipe, but you would not want to pulverize or demolish them.

Look at these examples of words with similar denotations but different connotations.

NEUTRAL	POSITIVE	NEGATIVE
absorbed	interested	obsessed
instill	inspire	indoctrinate
sufficient	ample	excessive

Remember that not all synonyms carry the same connotations. Some people might consider it a compliment to be called *resolute*, but if you called them *single-minded*, they might take offense. Although the words are synonymous, they trigger different emotions. Good writers stay sensitive to the ways their words can affect readers.

Shades of Meaning

Write a plus sign (+) in the box if the word has a positive connotation. Write a minus sign (–) it the word has a negative connotation. Put a zero (0) if the word is neutral.

1. residue ☐   2. cower ☐   3. ethical ☐   4. ostracize ☐

5. pseudonym ☐   6. addendum ☐   7. forthright ☐   8. promontory ☐

9. finesse ☐   10. asset ☐   11. porous ☐   12. flaunt ☐

13. disdain ☐   14. annul ☐   15. rehabilitate ☐   16. nonentity ☐

Expressing the Connotation

Read each sentence. Select the word in parentheses that better expresses the connotation (positive, negative, or neutral) given at the beginning of the sentence.

neutral **1.** The poet, known to be (**solitary, aloof**), spent months on a remote island in the Mediterranean.

negative **2.** After a brutal struggle, the dictator was finally (**dismissed, ousted**) from the palace.

negative **3.** The warranty will cover any (**problems, defects**) that appear during the first three months.

positive **4.** Cassie found out the hard way that other people don't always appreciate her (**biting, facetious**) comments.

negative **5.** Without any warning, the prisoner became irritable and (**volatile, impatient**), demanding to be released.

positive **6.** The con artist was (**blasé, relaxed**) about his role in the heist.

neutral **7.** Have you ever noticed that most TV butlers are (**staid, snobby**) and seldom talk?

positive **8.** In Paris, we kept going to the same restaurant to enjoy the wonderful meals that a renowned chef created with remarkable (**skill, finesse**).

Challenge: Using Connotation

*Choose vocabulary words from Units 4–6 to replace the **boldface** words in the sentences below. Then explain how the connotation of the replacement word changes the tone of the sentence.*

deplored	prodigal	pulverized
inaudible	mustered	ornate

1. Council members **grumbled about** _____ the outbreak of violence in areas close to schools.

_____

_____

2. Several of the old buildings still retained the **stylish** _____ ceilings and banisters that were typical of the eighteenth century.

_____

_____

3. During economic hardships, most people find **big** _____ spenders offensive.

_____

_____

Classical Roots

cur, curr, curs, cour—
to run

This Latin root appears in **recourse** (page 54). The original meaning was "a running back to," but the word now means "a turning to for help or protection" or "a source of help." Some other words based on the same root are listed below.

concourse	current	incur	recur
courier	discourse	precursor	recurrent

From the list of words above, choose the one that corresponds to each of the brief definitions below. Write the word in the blank space in the illustrative sentence below the definition. Use a dictionary if necessary.

1. to happen again, be repeated (*"run again"*)

Disturbing thoughts that _____ frequently may cause a person to seek help from a therapist.

2. to meet with, run into; to bring upon oneself (*"run into"*)

If you do not stick to a budget, you may _____ unnecessary debts.

3. a crowd; a thoroughfare; a place where crowds gather (*"running together"*)

We joined the _____ of people in the village square.

4. occurring or appearing repeatedly, returning regularly

Movie soundtracks often use several _____ musical themes.

5. to talk; a conversation; a long discussion on some topic

The featured speaker delivered a(n) _____ on using the Internet as a research tool.

6. a flow, movement; of the present time; in general use

My poem appears in the _____ issue of the school magazine.

7. a messenger, usually on urgent or official business

To ensure their safety, the top-secret letters were sent by diplomatic

_____.

8. a forerunner; that which precedes and shows the way

Ancient Athens is considered the _____ of modern democracy.

*Read the following passage, taking note of the **boldface** words and their contexts. These words are among those you will be studying in Unit 7. As you complete the exercises in this Unit, it may help to refer to the way the words are used below.*

The Discriminating Pigeon

<Magazine Article>

by C.W. Senghor

The **attribute** of intelligence is a difficult aspect of animal life to measure. **Predatory** behavior, courtship rituals, nesting instincts, and many other phenomena are relatively easy to describe. But there is no single accepted definition or **doctrine** of intelligence. Nevertheless, scientific experiments have demonstrated sophisticated learning, memory, and problem-solving behavior in a variety of animal species. The chimpanzee remains the **acme** of animal intelligence, with other **exotic** creatures, including dolphins and elephants, not far behind. Less well-known is the remarkable intelligence of the **unassuming** pigeon.

Experiments investigating pigeon intelligence date back sixty years. Few people would list the bird among the world's smartest animals. Some might even **belittle** the pigeon in this regard. But one has to give credit where credit is due. The body of evidence is growing so fast that scientists in the field of animal cognition are practically **wallowing** in data on the mental feats of these familiar birds. The results increasingly **convey** an impression of the pigeon as a curiously discriminating critter.

Experiments dating back to the 1980s indicate that pigeons perform better than most animals on the "mirror test." This test determines whether an animal can recognize its reflection in a mirror. Humans, chimpanzees, and other apes recognize their reflections without prior training, as do elephants and dolphins. Pigeons require training before they associate their reflections with their bodies. Nevertheless, that they can be trained to perform this way makes pigeons unusual. Of course, scientific interpretations of the mirror test have **wavered** over the years. But the study of self-recognition in animals reached a new **juncture** with experiments in which pigeons were alternately shown live and pre-recorded video images of themselves. The results, published in 2008 by Koji Toda and Shigeru Watanabe, indicate that pigeons can learn to distinguish between live and pre-recorded images of themselves. Self-recognition in pigeons remains a controversial issue. But these experiments support scientists who take a **stance** in favor of the claim that pigeons have a kind of self-awareness.

Professor Watanabe heads the Brain and Evolution unit of Japan's Keio University. Decades of research into animal minds are housed behind his beaming eyes and **jaunty** smile. Among Watanabe's and his colleagues' most intriguing work are experiments in which pigeons were trained to distinguish between paintings by Picasso and paintings by Monet. The trained pigeons could discriminate between paintings by the two artists with remarkable accuracy. In another experiment, pigeons were taught to distinguish between two groups of paintings by children. The first group of paintings had been judged by observers as "good" paintings, while the second group had been judged as "bad." The pigeons quickly learned the difference and accurately distinguished between "good" and "bad" when shown new paintings.

These experiments are remarkable. But there's little chance that pigeons will replace human art critics in making distinctions between the **tawdry** and the tasteful. The pigeon's ability to discriminate between different kinds of paintings, like its self-recognition, depends on prior training. Left on their own, pigeons don't recognize themselves in mirrors or seem to care much for art. Considerations like these might diminish our awe at the pigeon's mental powers. But there's no chance that the bird's brainy reputation will be entirely **ravaged**. The facts are in, and the pigeons have earned a place in the ranks of our planet's intelligent animals.

For iWords and audio passages, snap the code, or go to **vocabularyworkshop.com**.

Definitions

Note the spelling, pronunciation, part(s) of speech, and definition(s) of each of the following words. Then write the appropriate form of the word in the blank spaces in the illustrative sentence(s) following. Finally, study the lists of synonyms and antonyms.

1. acme
(ak′ mē)

(*n.*) the highest point

A perfect game is the _____ of any pitcher's career in baseball.

SYNONYMS: summit, top, peak, pinnacle
ANTONYMS: low point, bottom, nadir

2. attribute
(*n.,* at′ trə byüt; *v.,* ə trib′ yət)

(*n.*) a quality or characteristic belonging to or associated with someone or something; (*v.*) to assign to, credit with; to regard as caused by or resulting from

The _____ I most admire in you is your willingness to give everyone's opinions a fair hearing.

The doctor _____ my runny nose and itchy eyes to multiple allergies.

SYNONYMS: (*n.*) trait; (*v.*) ascribe

3. belittle
(bi lit′ əl)

(*v.*) to make something appear smaller than it is; to refer to in a way that suggests lack of importance or value

Candidates for public office may resort to negative ads that _____ their opponents' records.

SYNONYMS: minimize, underrate, disparage
ANTONYMS: exaggerate, magnify, overestimate

4. convey
(kən vā′)

(*v.*) to transport; to transmit; to communicate, make known; to transfer ownership or title to

Please _____ our best wishes to your parents on their twenty-fifth wedding anniversary.

SYNONYMS: carry, send, impart

5. doctrine
(däk′ trin)

(*n.*) a belief, principle, or teaching; a system of such beliefs or principles; a formulation of such beliefs or principles

No two religions see eye to eye on every fine detail of _____.

6. excise
(*v.,* ek sīz′; *n.,* ek′ sīz)

(*v.*) to remove by cutting; (*n.*) an indirect tax on the manufacture, sale, or distribution of a commodity or service

If you _____ that irrelevant remark, you will improve your essay.

The _____ imposed on products such as tobacco and alcohol have skyrocketed.

SYNONYMS: (*v.*) cut out, expunge
ANTONYMS: (*v.*) put in, interpolate

7. exotic
(ig zät' ik)

(*adj.*) foreign; charmingly unfamiliar or strikingly unusual

A recipe may call for _____ herbs and spices that are difficult to obtain.

SYNONYMS: strange, alien, picturesque, colorful
ANTONYMS: native, indigenous, familiar, commonplace

8. haggard
(hag' ərd)

(*adj.*) thin, pale, and careworn as a result of worry or suffering; wild-looking

The _____ refugees were given food, clothing, and temporary shelter.

SYNONYMS: drawn, gaunt, wasted
ANTONYMS: healthy, glowing, hale and hearty

9. jaunty
(jôn' tē)

(*adj.*) lively, easy, and carefree in manner; smart or trim in appearance

I bought a _____ straw hat.

SYNONYMS: unconcerned, lighthearted
ANTONYMS: downcast, dejected, glum

10. juncture
(jungk' chər)

(*n.*) a joining together; the point at which two things are joined; any important point in time

Our property ends at the _____ of the two stone walls.

SYNONYMS: union, seam, joint, turning point

11. menial
(mē' nē əl)

(*adj.*) lowly, humble, lacking importance or dignity; (*n.*) a person who does the humble and unpleasant tasks

During the Great Depression, people were thankful to have work of any kind, no matter how _____.

Teenagers in need of work can often find jobs as _____ in grocery stores and restaurants.

SYNONYMS: (*n.*) underling, scullion, servant
ANTONYMS: (*adj.*) lofty, elevated; (*n.*) boss, master

12. parry
(par' ē)

(*v.*) to ward off, fend off, evade, avoid; (*n.*) a defensive movement in fencing and other sports

An effective press secretary can _____ almost any question a reporter asks.

The challenger's swift _____ caught the champion completely off guard.

13. predatory
(pred' ə tôr ē)

(*adj.*) preying on, plundering, or piratical

Owls and other _____ birds play an important role in maintaining the balance of nature.

SYNONYMS: looting, pillaging, ravenous, rapacious

14. ravage
(rav′ ij)

(v.) to destroy, lay waste, ruin; (n.) ruinous damage, destruction

Swarms of locusts _____ the farmer's fields and orchards.

No one can escape the _____ of time.

SYNONYMS: (v.) wreck, devastate
ANTONYM: (v.) spare

15. stance
(stans)

(n.) a way of holding the body; an attitude or position on an issue

A fashion model's _____ is calculated to show off a designer's clothing to best advantage.

SYNONYMS: posture, bearing

16. tawdry
(tô′ drē)

(adj.) showy and flashy but lacking in good taste

An excess of gold braid and glittery beads gave the costumes a _____ look.

SYNONYMS: loud, gaudy, tacky, vulgar
ANTONYMS: refined, tasteful, subdued, muted

17. turncoat
(tərn′ kōt)

(n.) a person who switches to an opposing side or party

Strikers generally consider those workers who cross the picket lines to be _____.

SYNONYMS: quisling, deserter, renegade
ANTONYMS: loyalist, diehard

18. unassuming
(ən ə sü′ miŋ)

(adj.) not putting on airs, unpretentious; modest

Many celebrities remain _____ despite their fame and wealth.

ANTONYMS: conceited, pretentious, self-important

19. wallow
(wäl′ ō)

(v.) to roll about in a lazy, clumsy, or helpless way; to overindulge in; to have in abundance; (n.) a wet, muddy, or dusty area used by animals as a sort of bath; a state of moral or physical collapse

After a strenuous hike, I was too tired to do anything but _____ blissfully in a hot bath.

On the Serengeti Plain, _____ offer animals much-needed relief from the sun's scorching rays.

SYNONYMS: (v.) delight in, bask in

20. waver
(wā′ vər)

(v.) to move to and fro, become unsteady; to show lack of firmness or decision

The committee _____ for several days before choosing the winner of the essay contest.

SYNONYM: hesitate
ANTONYMS: stand firm, be resolute

Choosing the Right Word

Select the **boldface** word that better completes each sentence. You might refer to the passage on pages 88–89 to see how most of these words are used in context.

1. For many years the towns and villages along the Normandy coast of France showed the (**ravages, doctrines**) of the great invasion of 1944.

2. Instead of answering my question, the skillful debater (**parried, ravaged**) by asking a question of her own.

3. The captain was deeply worried, even though he tried hard to appear confident and (**haggard, jaunty**) to the passengers.

4. We were infuriated by the (**unassuming, tawdry**) speech in which he tried to portray himself as a great national leader.

General Dwight D. Eisenhower gave the orders for the Allied Invasion of Normandy.

5. My mother's dream vacation is to spend several weeks on a(n) (**exotic, menial**) island in the South Pacific.

6. After waiting for news of her loved ones for several days, the woman looked careworn and (**haggard, menial**).

7. The immigrants never (**excised, wavered**) in their determination to become American citizens.

8. Even after pitching two no-hit games this season, Stan was the same quiet and (**exotic, unassuming**) boy we had always known.

9. Thieves are essentially a (**predatory, jaunty**) class of criminals because they live off what they can take from others.

10. He hoped that election to the presidency would be the (**acme, juncture**) of his long and brilliant career in public service.

11. One must be careful these days, as (**excise, predatory**) phone calls from dishonest companies are on the rise.

12. During our trip to China, we sampled such (**predatory, exotic**) dishes as thousand-year-old eggs and bird's nest soup.

13. Americans expect candidates to take a definite (**stance, parry**) on each of the important issues in a national election.

14. So long as you continue to (**waver, wallow**) in self-pity, you will lack the strength needed to solve your problems.

15. When asked about your commitment to your values, do not (**waver, convey**), but stand firm in your beliefs.

16. I am thoroughly disgusted by people who try to make themselves seem more important than they really are by (**belittling, conveying**) others.

17. History teaches us that in any great conflict, there will be some (**turncoats, menials**) willing to go over to the enemy.

18. The general (**belittled, attributed**) our failure to win the battle to a lack of sufficient forces rather than to a lack of courage.

19. Did you know that pigs can't pant, so they (**ravage, wallow**) in mud to keep their bodies cool on hot summer days?

20. "If we are to keep the body politic healthy," the senator remarked, "we must (**excise, attribute**) the cancer of racial prejudice from it."

21. He is so conceited that it is hard to (**convey, wallow**) to him the simple idea that he did not win the essay competition.

22. Our system of justice is based on the (**acme, doctrine**) that defendants are presumed innocent unless the prosecution can prove them guilty.

23. No matter how (**menial, tawdry**) the assignment may be, take pride in your work, and do your best.

24. When I arrived at the critical (**stance, juncture**) in my career, I realized that my whole future would depend on the decision I was about to make.

25. My doctor (**attributed, parried**) my dizziness and vertigo to an inner ear infection.

Synonyms

*Choose the word from this Unit that is the same or most nearly the same in meaning as the **boldface** word or expression in the phrase. Write that word on the line. Use a dictionary if necessary.*

1. a closet filled with **garish** outfits _____

2. denounced as a **traitor** _____

3. **delete** an irrelevant clause _____

4. looking **exhausted** after a long trek _____

5. **demolished** by a series of storms _____

6. seldom **falters** under pressure _____

7. had an unpopular **point of view** _____

8. left the cleaning up to the **subordinates** _____

9. the **policy** of equal justice for all _____

10. sought to **deflect** the force of the assault _____

Antonyms

*Choose the word from this Unit that is most nearly opposite in meaning to the **boldface** word or expression in the phrase. Write that word on the line. Use a dictionary if necessary.*

1. **insert** the word *crucial*　　　　　　　　　　＿＿＿＿＿＿＿＿＿＿

2. undertaking a **grand** endeavor　　　　　　　＿＿＿＿＿＿＿＿＿＿

3. an **advocate** for women's rights　　　　　　＿＿＿＿＿＿＿＿＿＿

4. someone who can **attract** a large audience　＿＿＿＿＿＿＿＿＿＿

5. a **radiant** expression on her face　　　　　　＿＿＿＿＿＿＿＿＿＿

Completing the Sentence

From the words in this Unit, choose the one that best completes each of the following sentences. Write the correct word form in the space provided.

1. We will need several trucks to ＿＿＿＿＿＿＿＿＿＿ all the books to the new library building.

2. The room was so overcrowded with gaudy furnishings that the overall effect was cheap and ＿＿＿＿＿＿＿＿＿＿.

3. The author's first published work was a(n) ＿＿＿＿＿＿＿＿＿＿ little pamphlet on the joys of fly fishing.

4. During our trip through Kenya, we took many pictures of hippos as they ＿＿＿＿＿＿＿＿＿＿ in a mudhole.

5. Her happy expression and the ＿＿＿＿＿＿＿＿＿＿ way she walked down the street gave the impression of someone "on top of the world."

6. I agree that we should not exaggerate her achievements, but we should not ＿＿＿＿＿＿＿＿＿＿ them either.

7. A baseball player who improves his ＿＿＿＿＿＿＿＿＿＿ at the plate usually improves his batting average, too.

8. When he switched parties, people called him a(n) ＿＿＿＿＿＿＿＿＿＿, but he claimed he'd just had an honest change of opinion.

9. Since my boss has, as they say, "a short fuse," patience cannot be considered one of her outstanding ＿＿＿＿＿＿＿＿＿＿.

10. The Monroe ＿＿＿＿＿＿＿＿＿＿ sought to prevent the colonization of the American continents by European powers.

11. She sat there staring at the menu, _____ between the steak sandwich and the chef's salad.

12. In her most celebrated novels, such as *Pride and Prejudice* and *Emma*, Jane Austen reached the _____ of her literary art.

13. Because of his ability to _____ his opponents' blows, he was rarely hurt in his many fights in the ring.

14. In the early nineteenth century, Thomas Bowdler attempted to "clean up" the works of Shakespeare by _____ all words and phrases that he felt were coarse or offensive.

15. Even though you are starting at a(n) _____ job, you will gain valuable experience and knowledge of how the company works.

16. Though many _____ creatures prefer to hunt at night, lions and leopards are active during the daytime.

17. Two of our divisions were marching rapidly toward each other and hoped to effect a(n) _____ before the enemy attacked.

18. Disease had so _____ his once-handsome face that I scarcely recognized him!

19. Most Americans think of Australia as a strange and wonderful continent full of _____ plants and animals.

20. The drawn and _____ faces of the rescued miners clearly reflected the terrible ordeal they had survived.

Writing: Words in Action

1. Look back at "The Discriminating Pigeon" (pages 88–89). Suppose that you work with Professor Watanabe. He has asked you to write an article for a local newspaper. The purpose of your article is to persuade readers that pigeons are not public nuisances but are in fact truly brilliant creatures. In your article, summarize Dr. Watanabe's findings, and make a strong case for the intelligence of the pigeon. Write the article, using at least two details from the passage and three Unit words to support your claim.

2. Can animals think? For many, this question has yet to be answered. Skeptics claim that though animals can be trained, they cannot think. Some scientists, though, maintain that animals *can* think, and that they can even be creative and solve problems. From researchers to animal trainers to pet owners, people hold a wide range of opinions on this issue. What is your stance? In a brief essay, state your opinion and support it with evidence from the reading (refer to pages 88–89) or from your own observations, studies, or experience. Write at least three paragraphs, and use three or more words from this Unit.

Vocabulary in Context

Literary Text

The following excerpts are from Little Women *by Louisa May Alcott. Some of the words you have studied in this Unit appear in* **boldface** *type. Complete each statement below the excerpt by circling the letter of the correct answer.*

1. If Jo had only known what a great happiness was **wavering** in the balance for one of them, she would have turned dove-like in a minute, but unfortunately, we . . . cannot see what goes on in the minds of our friends.

    The act of **wavering** involves
    - **a.** standing firm
    - **b.** hoping
    - **c.** changing course
    - **d.** departing

2. The war is over, and Mr. March safely at home, busy with his books and the small parish which found in him a minister by nature as by grace, a quiet, studious man, rich in the wisdom that is better than learning, the charity which calls all mankind "brother," the piety that blossoms into character, making it august and lovely.

    These **attributes**, in spite of poverty and the strict integrity which shut him out from the more worldly successes, attracted to him many admirable persons . . . .

    An **attribute** is a(n)
    - **a.** rumor
    - **b.** feature
    - **c.** obligation
    - **d.** difficulty

3. With that Jo marched straight away and the rest followed, a bright little band of sisters, all looking their best in summer suits, with happy faces under the **jaunty** hatbrims.

    Something that is **jaunty** is NOT
    - **a.** jolly
    - **b.** balanced
    - **c.** stylish
    - **d.** somber

4. The screne Teuton found the supper-table and was happy, eating steadily through the bill of fare, and dismayed the garçons by the **ravages** he committed.

    Ravages are most likely
    - **a.** destructive
    - **b.** reassuring
    - **c.** invisible
    - **d.** admired

June Allyson plays Jo and Peter Lawford plays Laurie in this 1949 film adaptation of *Little Women.*

5. "This **unassuming** style promotes study, that's why we adopt it," returned Laurie, who certainly could not be accused of vanity, having voluntarily sacrificed a handsome curly crop to the demand for quarter-inch-long stubble.

    A style that is **unassuming** is
    - **a.** showy
    - **b.** formal
    - **c.** plain
    - **d.** crude

Snap the code, or go to **vocabularyworkshop.com**

*Read the following passage, taking note of the **boldface** words and their contexts. These words are among those you will be studying in Unit 8. As you complete the exercises in this Unit, it may help to refer to the way the words are used below.*

Aquatic Robotics
<Technical Essay>

Two-thirds of Earth's surface is covered with water. Human beings have yet to **infiltrate** most of this unexplored and **cryptic** terrain. Instead, their most important **proxies** underwater are robots. The field of undersea robotics has grown rapidly in recent years. It is now an essential part of ocean exploration.

At the very foundation of robot design is the performance of tasks that are difficult, repetitive, or dangerous. These same words describe undersea exploration. For example, the important missions of marine research often require a descent to great depths. Vast areas of the ocean floor remain inaccessible to humans no matter what protective **attire** they wear or equipment they use. And no eager explorer, however **fervent**, would carry out a deep diving **stint** lasting months at a time.

Robotics engineers began to pick up on these challenges in the 1990s. They channeled their efforts into developing three **divergent** types of undersea robots. One type is a remote-controlled vehicle that is towed behind ships. Another type is really a miniature submarine that carries a human crew and is equipped with robot arms. A third type of robot is fully autonomous, carrying out a survey in an **unflagging** fashion that no human could hope to match.

The movement of the robot *Ariel* is based on how actual crabs move.

Undersea robots are designed to aid humans in a variety of endeavors. Some of these are ecological. For instance, an early objective of the *Odyssey* robot series that was developed at the Massachusetts Institute of Technology was to investigate the decreasing number of humpback whales on Stellwagen Bank, a large underwater plateau at the mouth of Massachusetts Bay. Another *Odyssey* mission took the robot to the bottom of the Labrador Sea between Newfoundland and Greenland. There, even the notoriously rough winter weather could not **nullify** the robot's mission to explore ocean oxygenation. In this process, surface waters in high latitudes near the poles become oxygen-rich but also cold and dense. The cold, dense water **plummets** to the bottom in plumes, where it provides energy for many kinds of life. Without *Odyssey*'s assistance in such missions, human efforts would have been to no **avail**, given the conditions. The latest *Odyssey* robot can even hover in place, like a helicopter. It can be controlled remotely with a joystick.

Scientists are not the only ones using aquatic robots. Undersea robots are also important for military uses. The robot crab *Ariel*, for example, may be used to clear mines from minefields that **abut** the shore. No obstacle or crevice stops *Ariel*. Few humans would remain calm and **stoical** performing such a hazardous duty. Military robots are also used to find enemy submarines and to protect coastal areas.

At present, there is virtually no **perceptible** limit on the array of uses for undersea robotics. The British independent robot *Autosub4*, for example, has been used to explore herring behavior in the North Sea and to locate valuable metals at the bottom of a Scottish lake. Tethered underwater vehicles called ROVs have assisted marine archaeologists in locating and exploring shipwrecks, including that of the *Titanic*. And after the massive Gulf oil spill disaster in 2010, cleanup analyses and efforts relied heavily on ROVs. It is safe to **proclaim** that undersea exploration in the twenty-first century will increasingly be the domain of robots as they go where humans cannot hope to follow.

Audio

For iWords and audio passages, snap the code, or go to **vocabularyworkshop.com**.

Definitions

Note the spelling, pronunciation, part(s) of speech, and definition(s) of each of the following words. Then write the appropriate form of the word in the blank spaces in the illustrative sentence(s) following. Finally, study the lists of synonyms and antonyms.

1. abut
(ə bət′)

(v.) to join at one end or be next to; to support, prop up

Land that _____ a river or lake is considered a highly desirable location on which to build a summer home.

SYNONYMS: border on, bolster

2. attire
(ə tīr′)

(n.) clothes, apparel, garb; (v.) to dress, adorn, or bedeck

The special _____ that firefighters wear helps to protect them from flames and smoke.

The children happily _____ their stuffed animals in holiday outfits and accessories.

SYNONYM: (n.) clothing

3. avail
(ə vāl′)

(v.) to be of use or benefit to; to make use of; to take advantage of; to profit or benefit; (n.) use, benefit, or value

Be sure to _____ yourself of all the services that the school library has to offer.

I tried repeatedly to contact my neighbor by phone, but to absolutely no _____.

4. crony
(krō′ nē)

(n.) a very close friend, chum, buddy

We have been _____ ever since we met in the second grade.

ANTONYMS: adversary, rival

5. cryptic
(krip′ tik)

(adj.) puzzling, mystifying, or enigmatic

The letter to the editor was so _____ that I couldn't be certain what the writer had actually intended to say.

ANTONYMS: crystal clear, unambiguous

6. divergent
(də vər′ jənt)

(adj.) going in different directions; different from each other; departing from convention, deviant

Two people may be close friends despite their having very _____ interests and beliefs.

SYNONYMS: not in agreement, differing, unorthodox, unconventional
ANTONYMS: merging, intersecting, converging, orthodox, conventional

7. enmity
(en' mə tē)

(*n.*) hatred, ill-will

Despite a long, close, and tense match, the defeated player felt no _____ toward the new champion.

SYNONYMS: hostility, animosity
ANTONYMS: friendship, amity

8. fervent
(fər' vənt)

(*adj.*) very earnest, emotional, passionate; extremely hot

The president delivered a _____ plea for tolerance and unity.

SYNONYMS: enthusiastic, burning, blazing, scorching
ANTONYMS: blasé, apathetic, restrained, emotionless

9. gaunt
(gônt)

(*adj.*) thin and bony, starved looking; bare, barren

We left food and water for the _____ alley cat.

SYNONYMS: lean, lanky, all skin and bones
ANTONYMS: plump, stout, corpulent

10. infiltrate
(in' fil trāt)

(*v.*) to pass through or gain entrance to gradually or stealthily

Some of our men _____ the enemy's camp and captured their leader.

SYNONYMS: slip into, creep into, penetrate

11. nullify
(nəl' ə fī)

(*v.*) to make of no value or consequence, cancel, wipe out

After seven days, you cannot _____ the contract without being charged a penalty.

SYNONYMS: invalidate, annul
ANTONYMS: confirm, endorse, ratify, sanction

12. perceptible
(pər sep' tə bəl)

(*adj.*) capable of being grasped by the senses or mind

There was no _____ improvement in the patient's condition despite the doctors' best efforts to treat the infection.

SYNONYMS: noticeable, discernible, observable
ANTONYMS: invisible, unnoticeable, indiscernible

13. plummet
(pləm' ət)

(*v.*) to plunge straight down; (*n.*) a weight fastened to a line

Gannets and other seabirds _____ headfirst into the ocean to catch small fish and squid.

Experts think the pierced round stones found at the site served as _____ to weight fishing nets.

SYNONYM: (*v.*) take a nosedive
ANTONYMS: (*v.*) soar, skyrocket

14. proclaim
(prō klām')

(v.) to declare publicly or officially

We _____ loyalty to our country when we recite the Pledge of Allegiance.

SYNONYMS: announce, promulgate
ANTONYMS: conceal, cover up

15. proxy
(präk' sē)

(n.) an agent, substitute; a written permission allowing one person to act in another's place

The vice president may be called upon to be the president's _____ at the funeral of a foreign leader.

SYNONYM: deputy

16. rankle
(raη' kəl)

(v.) to cause anger, irritation, or bitterness (with the suggestion that the pain grows worse with time)

Insults may _____ a person for many years.

SYNONYMS: irritate, vex, nettle, irk
ANTONYMS: please, gratify

17. scavenger
(skav' ən jər)

(n.) a person who collects or removes usable items from waste materials; an animal that feeds on refuse or dead bodies

A few _____ such as catfish and other bottom feeders will help to keep a fish tank clean.

SYNONYM: rummager

18. stint
(stint)

(v.) to limit, be sparing or frugal; (n.) a limit or restriction; a fixed share of work or duty; a period of activity

Good hosts never _____ on food and drink for the guests who attend their parties.

A _____ as the guest host of a popular talk show may be a big career break for a young comedian.

SYNONYMS: (v.) restrict, scrimp, economize
ANTONYMS: (v.) splurge, squander, lavish

19. stoical
(stō' i kəl)

(adj.) self-controlled, not showing feeling in response to pleasure or pain

The refugees' _____ acceptance of their plight was deeply moving.

SYNONYMS: unresponsive, impassive
ANTONYMS: excitable, emotional, hotheaded

20. unflagging
(ən flag' iη)

(adj.) tireless, continuing with vigor

After the votes were counted, the candidates paid tribute to the _____ loyalty of their supporters.

SYNONYMS: steady, undiminished, unremitting
ANTONYMS: diminishing, drooping, sagging

Choosing the Right Word

Select the **boldface** word that better completes each sentence. You might refer to the passage on pages 98–99 to see how most of these words are used in context.

1. In the unforgettable words of the Declaration of Independence, Jefferson (**proclaimed, rankled**) to the world that a new nation had been born.

2. The (**unflagging, gaunt**) and leafless trees seemed to add to the gloom of that wintry scene.

3. We gave strict instructions to the work crew, telling them that, when they install the countertop, they must make sure that it (**abuts, plummets**) the wall.

4. The two candidates are working hard to get the voters' support, but in my opinion there is no (**perceptible, cryptic**) difference between them.

5. Our hopes for a winning touchdown (**availed, plummeted**) in the last minute when Jim fumbled and South High recovered the ball.

Thomas Jefferson was not only a talented writer, but also an accomplished scientist and inventor.

6. Although the woman was filled with grief, she remained (**gaunt, stoical**) during the poignant memorial service.

7. I pretended that being ignored by the "best people in town" meant nothing to me, but actually those snubs (**rankled, nullified**) deeply.

8. During the prolonged dry spell, the farmers' (**fervent, perceptible**) prayers for rain were seldom answered.

9. Let me state my absolute (**stoicism, enmity**) for those who seek to bring about political change through violent means.

10. Our farm used to (**stint, abut**) the high school football field, but now a highway separates the two tracts of land.

11. All the heroism of our men could not (**abut, avail**) against the enemy's superior forces.

12. Large numbers of stockholders allowed (**scavengers, proxies**) to vote in their place.

13. It is a sad fact of experience that postwar political blunders can often (**nullify, infiltrate**) or even reverse the results of battlefield triumphs.

14. In a democracy, we expect people to have (**gaunt, divergent**) views and to express them openly.

15. We made phone calls, sent e-mails, and combed the neighborhood on foot, but our search for the lost dog was to no (**stint, avail**).

16. After the big snowstorm, the trees seemed to be (**attired, cronies**) in white lace.

17. In spite of my efforts to keep them at bay, spring weeds always manage to (**infiltrate, proclaim**) my vegetable garden.

18. When the temperature suddenly (**plummeted, nullified**) to below freezing, the hikers made the wise decision to descend the mountain.

19. President Kennedy bore his pain in such a (**perceptible, stoical**) manner that few people realized how much he suffered from his World War II back injury.

20. I understand that pigeons are (**plummets, scavengers**) by nature, but I still don't like them pecking around our picnic table, looking for crumbs.

21. If we had a good civil service system in this town, the mayor wouldn't be able to put his (**cronies, enmities**) on the public payroll.

22. Before going to college, my brother did a (**stint, proxy**) as an apprentice radio operator on an oceangoing tanker.

23. For her (**unflagging, divergent**) devotion to every good cause in our community, we honor this wonderful woman.

24. It didn't take me long to master the (**fervent, cryptic**) greetings, signs, and handshakes that were part of the club's rituals.

25. The moon is sometimes faintly (**proxy, perceptible**) in the morning sky.

Synonyms

*Choose the word from this Unit that is the same or most nearly the same in meaning as the **boldface** word or expression in the phrase. Write that word on the line. Use a dictionary if necessary.*

1. left out for **foragers** to sift through   _____

2. an **ardent** advocate for the poor   _____

3. selected to act as my **representative**   _____

4. a lack of respect that **galls**   _____

5. packed **outfits** suitable for all kinds of weather   _____

6. plan to visit an old **pal**   _____

7. lingering **antagonism** despite the settlement   _____

8. forced to **cut back** even on necessities   _____

9. **broadcast** my intention to run for office   _____

10. as **scrawny** as a skeleton   _____

Antonyms

*Choose the word from this Unit that is most nearly opposite in meaning to the **boldface** word or expression in the phrase. Write that word on the line. Use a dictionary if necessary.*

1. a valued **alliance** _____

2. trying to **delight** the audience _____

3. keep your **enemies** close _____

4. the **prey** will become food _____

5. a healthy but **hefty** dachshund _____

Completing the Sentence

From the words in this Unit, choose the one that best completes each of the following sentences. Write the correct word form in the space provided.

1. Over a period of years, words and phrases used in the field of computer science _____ everyday speech.

2. His failure to win the election _____ in his mind until it caused a complete emotional breakdown.

3. In our community, people of many ethnic backgrounds work together without jealousy or _____.

4. My father has three _____ who go with him each year on a camping trip in the High Sierras.

5. All her efforts to get more business for her troubled company proved to be of no _____, and the store had to close down.

6. To prepare for the job interview, she _____ herself in a simple but elegant navy blue suit.

7. I didn't think she would have the nerve to ask me for a loan, but she did—and with no _____ embarrassment.

8. The witnesses' statements are so _____ that it's hard to know how the accident actually happened.

9. Each year the president _____ the last Thursday in November as a day of national thanksgiving.

10. We decided not to buy the house, mainly because the property it sits on unfortunately _____ the noisy main highway.

11. Shakespeare said that Cassius had a "lean and hungry look," but I would describe him with the single word _____.

12. The rise in the cost of living _____ my efforts to save some money from my small salary.

13. Although the vulture has a decidedly poor reputation, it does a useful job as a(n) _____, clearing away decaying matter.

14. Even after he retired and we expected him to slow down, his efforts in support of his beloved school remained _____.

15. Instead of giving us a clear and helpful answer, the speaker offered only the _____ prophecy that "time will tell."

16. As a teenager, she developed a(n) _____ interest in biology that led to a lifelong career.

17. We watched in dismay as our new model airplane suddenly went out of control and _____ to the ground.

18. Their parents had _____ for many years to save the money needed to send the children to college.

19. Since I will not be able to attend the meeting, I hereby appoint Ms. Brown to act as my _____.

20. He tried to appear _____ when he heard the bad news, but I realized that he was deeply hurt.

Writing: Words in Action

1. Look back at "Aquatic Robotics" (pages 98–99). How do you think aquatic robots and deep sea exploration will change our lives? Will they lead to improvements? If so, what benefits might they yield? Write a newspaper editorial expressing your views on the potential of aquatic robots. Use at least two details from the passage and three Unit words to support your ideas.

2. In addition to exploring the deep seas, robots are also being used in the workplace. Instead of people performing specific tasks, robots do the work. Robots can be found in factories, offices, hospitals, and research facilities. What is your opinion about robots in the workplace? Are there some tasks that robots can do better or more safely than humans, or is robot labor just another money-saving device that will put people out of jobs? Write a brief essay in which you state your position on this topic and support it with information from the reading (refer to pages 98–99), your own observations, your knowledge, or your personal experience. Write at least three paragraphs, and use three or more words from this Unit.

Vocabulary in Context

Literary Text

The following excerpts are from The Monster and Other Stories *and* The Red Badge of Courage *by Stephen Crane. Some of the words you have studied in this Unit appear in* **boldface** *type. Complete each statement below the excerpt by circling the letter of the correct answer.*

1. He grinned fraternally when he saw Jimmie coming. These two were pals. In regard to almost everything in life they seemed to have minds precisely alike. Of course there were points of emphatic **divergence**. ("The Monster," from *The Monster and Other Stories*)

    A **divergence** is a
    a. conversation
    b. euphemism
    c. falsehood
    d. disagreement

2. "Mr. Scully," called the Swede, "how much do I owe you?" It was seen that he was **attired** for departure, and that he had his valise in his hand. ("The Blue Hotel" from *The Monster and Other Stories*)

    To be **attired** is to be
    a. clothed
    b. organized
    c. unprepared
    d. annoyed

3. The **gaunt**, careworn features and dusty figures were made plain by this quaint light at the dawning, but it dressed the skin of the men in corpse-like hues and made the tangled limbs appear pulseless and dead. (*The Red Badge of Courage*)

    A person described as **gaunt** appears
    a. tireless
    b. fierce
    c. withered
    d. dangerous

4. The men, pitching forward insanely, had burst into cheerings, moblike and barbaric, but tuned in strange keys that can arouse the dullard and the **stoic**. (*The Red Badge of Courage*)

    One who is **stoic** is NOT
    a. tolerant
    b. emotional
    c. disciplined
    d. patient

Audie Murphy plays the young soldier in this film adaptation of *The Red Badge of Courage.*

5. These parts of the opposing armies were two long waves that pitched upon each other madly at dictated points. To and fro they swelled. Sometimes, one side by its yells and cheers would **proclaim** decisive blows, but a moment later the other side would be all yells and cheers. (*The Red Badge of Courage*)

    To **proclaim** is to
    a. gesture
    b. incorporate
    c. publicize
    d. conceal

Interactive Quiz

Snap the code, or go to **vocabularyworkshop.com**

*Read the following passage, taking note of the **boldface** words and their contexts. These words are among those you will be studying in Unit 9. As you complete the exercises in this Unit, it may help to refer to the way the words are used below.*

Tecumseh of the Shawnee
<Biographical Sketch>

Tecumseh

The great Shawnee leader, Tecumseh (Shooting Star), was born in 1768 in Ohio country. Like the land he was born to, the 45 years of his life were marked by war. Control of the fertile region had been contested for centuries, even before Europeans arrived. By the time Tecumseh was born, the British were the region's dominant power. British settlement continued to expand westward, **encroaching** on tribal lands. Irritated tribal leaders **chafed** at the expansion, and some sought to **fend** off the tide of settlers with violence. One of these leaders was Tecumseh's father, who was killed in a battle with the British in 1774. Soon after, the Shawnee sided with the British against the American colonies in the Revolutionary War.

When the Revolutionary War ended in 1783, Tecumseh was 15 years old. American forces continued to clash with tribes in Ohio and the surrounding region in a prolonged conflict referred to as the Northwest Indian War. Tecumseh fought in many battles and became the leader of a band of Shawnee warriors. The Northwest Indian War ended in 1794, with the Native Americans forced to **capitulate** and hand over most of the Ohio lands to the United States. Tensions between the native tribes and settlers cooled. Many tribal leaders even encouraged their people to adopt aspects of the settlers' culture.

This period of relative calm did not last long. Many Native Americans remained **disgruntled** at the spread of settlements and the now **predominant** U.S. authority that allowed settlers to take land with **impunity**. A true warrior never seeks glory, but by 1808, Tecumseh had emerged as a leader of **renown**. He travelled throughout the region to build an alliance strong enough to confront the United States. In his new role as a political leader, Tecumseh was a **prodigy**. He was a talented and **disarming** speaker, full of poise and

William Henry Harrison c. 1812

purpose. **Endowed** with an impressive physique, he presented a charismatic **mien**. He won thousands over to his cause. Tecumseh's Confederacy, as it came to be known, drew together many tribes.

The situation grew **dire** with the signing of the Treaty of Fort Wayne, which opened some 3 million acres of land to U.S. settlers. Tecumseh and 400 warriors met with Governor William Henry Harrison of the Indiana Territory to demand the treaty be nullified. When Harrison refused, Tecumseh headed south to recruit more allies for his Confederacy. Tribal forces carried out scattered raids on white settlers. While Tecumseh was away, Harrison led about 1,000 militia and army troops to Prophetstown. There he defeated the main force of Tecumseh's Confederacy at the Battle of Tippecanoe on November 7, 1811. Memory of that victory would serve Harrison well decades later as he sought to become the ninth president. Tecumseh, on the other hand, saw his plans begin to go **awry**. The Confederacy, **bludgeoned** by the defeat, would now take more time to develop.

As Tecumseh set out to rebuild the Confederacy, the War of 1812 broke out between Britain and the United States. The conflicts in the Northwest were one of the leading causes of this war, as many in the United States blamed the British for inciting the Indians to violence and supplying them with firearms. Tecumseh sided with the British and helped them defeat the Americans at Detroit. About a year later, Tecumseh was killed during the Battle of the Thames on October 5, 1813. His Confederacy surrendered soon after, giving the United States control over the Northwest frontier.

Audio

For iWords and audio passages, snap the code, or go to **vocabularyworkshop.com**.

Definitions

Note the spelling, pronunciation, part(s) of speech, and definition(s) of each of the following words. Then write the appropriate form of the word in the blank spaces in the illustrative sentence(s) following. Finally, study the lists of synonyms and antonyms.

1. apt
(apt)

(*adj.*) suitable, fitting, likely; quick to learn

The appropriate greeting card for a particular occasion is one that expresses _____ sentiments.

SYNONYMS: appropriate, fit, liable
ANTONYMS: inappropriate, slow

2. awry
(ə rī′)

(*adj., adv.*) in a turned or twisted position or direction; wrong, out of the right or hoped-for course

After running to catch the bus, I realized that my clothing was all _____.

If something went _____ during a countdown, NASA officials would cancel a shuttle launch.

SYNONYMS: (*adj.*) crooked, askew, amiss
ANTONYMS: (*adj.*) straight, symmetrical

3. bludgeon
(bləj′ ən)

(*n.*) a short club used as a weapon; (*v.*) to strike with a heavy club; to use force or strong arguments to gain some point

Early humans fashioned _____ from the thick limbs of trees.

Heavy-handed writers tend to _____ readers with explanations of their characters' motives.

SYNONYMS: (*n.*) cudgel; (*v.*) clobber, clout

4. capitulate
(kə pich′ ə lāt)

(*v.*) to end resistance, give up, throw in the towel

When I saw that I had been outmaneuvered by my opponent, I had no choice but to _____.

ANTONYMS: hold out, persist

5. chafe
(chāf)

(*v.*) to warm by rubbing; to wear sore by rubbing; to feel annoyance or dissatisfaction, annoy, irk; to strain or press against; (*n.*) a sore or injury caused by rubbing

The American colonists _____ under the many unjust laws imposed on them by King George III.

To keep that raw _____ from becoming infected, you should put a clean bandage on it.

SYNONYMS: (*v.*) irritate, scrape, abrade
ANTONYMS: (*v.*) soothe, mollify, please, elate

6. defile
(di fīl')

(*v., trans.*) to make unclean or dirty, destroy the purity of;
(*v., intrans.*) to march in a single line or in columns; (*n.*) a narrow passage; gorge, canyon

Those who _____ a house of worship will be punished to the full extent of the law.

The victorious troops _____ for review.

We hiked through the rocky _____.

SYNONYMS: (*v., trans.*) pollute, contaminate
ANTONYMS: (*v., trans.*) cleanse, purify

7. dire
(dīr)

(*adj.*) dreadful, causing fear or suffering; warning of trouble to come; demanding immediate action to avoid disaster

Environmentalists warn of the _____ consequences of the destruction of the world's rain forests.

SYNONYMS: disastrous, ominous, sinister, urgent
ANTONYMS: favorable, auspicious, beneficial

8. disarming
(dis ärm' iŋ)

(*adj.*) charming, tending to soften unfriendliness or suspicion

My best friend has a most _____ smile.

SYNONYMS: endearing, winning
ANTONYMS: alarming, troubling, disquieting

9. disgruntled
(dis grənt' əld)

(*adj., part*) in bad humor, discontented, annoyed

When flights are delayed because of bad weather, airline passengers may become extremely

_____.

SYNONYMS: displeased, grumpy, surly
ANTONYMS: pleased, satisfied, content

10. encroach
(en krōch')

(*v.*) to advance beyond the usual or proper limits, trespass

Where suburbs _____ on unspoiled forests or wetlands, delicate ecosystems may be disrupted.

SYNONYMS: intrude, infringe

11. endow
(en daú')

(*v.*) to furnish, equip, provide with funds or some other desirable thing or quality

Wealthy individuals often make provisions in their wills to _____ their favorite charities.

SYNONYMS: grant, bestow, present, bequeath
ANTONYMS: take away, deprive

12. fend
(fend)

(*v.*) to ward off, resist; to get along, manage

The picnic was enjoyable, but we spent quite a bit of time _____ off ants and mosquitos.

SYNONYMS: stave off, cope

13. impunity
(im pyü' nə tē)

(*n.*) freedom from punishment
Bullies must be made to realize that they cannot push other people around with _____.
SYNONYMS: exemption from penalty, immunity

14. mien
(mēn)

(*n.*) air, manner; appearance; expression
A person may adopt a cheerful _____ in an attempt to conceal sorrow or anger.
SYNONYMS: look, bearing

15. penal
(pē' nəl)

(*adj.*) having to do with punishment
Devil's Island, off the coast of French Guiana, was once the site of an infamous _____ colony.
SYNONYM: disciplinary

16. pertinent
(pər' tə nənt)

(*adj.*) related to the matter at hand, to the point
The joke you told was very amusing, but I fail to see how it was _____ to the conversation.
SYNONYMS: germane, apropos
ANTONYMS: unrelated, irrelevant, immaterial

17. predominant
(pri däm' ə nənt)

(*adj.*) the greatest in strength or power; most common
Cy Young, for whom the coveted pitching award is named, was once the _____ pitcher in baseball.
SYNONYMS: chief, major, paramount, prevalent
ANTONYMS: secondary, minor, subsidiary, rare

18. prodigy
(präd' ə jē)

(*n.*) something wonderful or marvelous; an unusual feat; a child or young person with extraordinary ability or talent
The careers of some musical _____ have turned out to be short-lived.
SYNONYMS: marvel, wonder, genius
ANTONYMS: dumbbell, dunce, dullard

19. recluse
(re' klüs)

(*n.*) a person who leads a life shut up or withdrawn from the world
An individual who has suffered a great emotional loss may become something of a _____.
SYNONYM: hermit

20. renown
(ri naùn')

(*n.*) fame, glory
Some writers earn acclaim during their lifetime, but others win _____ only after their death.
SYNONYMS: reputation, celebrity, prestige
ANTONYMS: obscurity, infamy, notoriety

Choosing the Right Word

*Select the **boldface** word that better completes each sentence. You might refer to the passage on pages 108–109 to see how most of these words are used in context.*

1. Some great composers, including Mozart and Mendelssohn, were (**pertinent, apt**) musicians from a very early age, demonstrating an amazing talent for writing music.

2. During the winter the wind usually blows from the north in that area, but during the summer southerly currents are (**predominant, awry**).

3. After a horrible accident, the one-time celebrity lived his life as a (**prodigy, recluse**), permanently turning his back on public life.

4. His plain clothing and quiet (**prodigy, mien**) were not what we expected in a famous Hollywood director.

5. Why does she (**bludgeon, capitulate**) people she barely knows with her arguments and strong opinions?

Mozart began composing slow, elegant dance tunes called minuets at the age of five.

6. The Declaration of Independence mentions a number of "unalienable rights" with which all people "are (**endowed, chafed**) by their Creator."

7. The college my sister attends is a small one, but it has gained a great deal of (**recluse, renown**) for the quality of its faculty.

8. The injured quarterback (**chafed, defiled**) at sitting on the bench while his team was being badly beaten on the field.

9. Nature is kind to us in many ways, but we must learn that we cannot violate its laws with (**impunity, renown**).

10. Although the child was terrified of shots, the skillful nurse (**capitulated, disarmed**) the weeping boy by singing a funny song.

11. Do you understand how someone can live as a (**mien, recluse**) even in the midst of a great city?

12. The lecturer is a man who served ten years in prison and is now devoting his life to bringing about reforms in our (**penal, predominant**) system.

13. Yes, we are still friends, but not as close as we used to be; something has gone (**awry, dire**) in our relationship.

14. Mosses and lichens—which can survive extremely cold temperatures—are (**predominant, dire**) plants in the Arctic tundra.

15. Marie is (**apt, endowed**) to forget where she puts important things, such as her keys, wallet, and glasses.

16. He claims to be a patriot, but his disregard for the powerless (**encroaches, defiles**) the great ideals on which this nation was built.

17. The message of a great work of literature may be as (**pertinent, disgruntled**) today as it was when it was first written.

18. My problem was to (**fend, bludgeon**) off their unwelcome attentions without being openly insulting.

19. As we use up the earth's fossil-fuel supplies, we are faced with an increasingly (**disarming, dire**) need to develop new energy sources.

20. I was so (**chafed, disarmed**) by the way he asked for a loan that to my surprise I found myself giving him the money.

21. When the featured singer failed to appear, the (**disgruntled, apt**) fans demanded their money back.

22. A team as determined as ours is will never (**capitulate, endow**), even if it is losing badly in the final moments of a game.

23. Alvin York performed such (**impunities, prodigies**) on the battlefields of France that he was awarded this nation's highest honors.

24. The rights guaranteed by the U.S. Constitution do not permit citizens to (**fend, encroach**) on the rights of others.

25. The starch in this shirt collar is (**disarming, chafing**) my neck.

Synonyms

*Choose the word from this Unit that is the same or most nearly the same in meaning as the **boldface** word or expression in the phrase. Write that word on the line. Use a dictionary if necessary.*

1. further **aggravated** our already strained nerves   _____

2. a gruff **demeanor** but a kindly heart   _____

3. obtain all the **relevant** documents   _____

4. paid a **proper** tribute   _____

5. had a reputation for being a **loner**   _____

6. trespassed with apparent **amnesty**   _____

7. **gave up** after a long and exhausting struggle   _____

8. a crime that **desecrates** the nation's honor   _____

9. fought all attempts to **invade** our privacy   _____

10. sent the defendant to a **correctional** facility   _____

Antonyms

*Choose the word from this Unit that is most nearly opposite in meaning to the **boldface** word or expression in the phrase. Write that word on the line. Use a dictionary if necessary.*

1. used a **nonpunitive** method of teaching _____

2. an **unlikely** action _____

3. considered to be a **random** comment _____

4. to **revere** the natural beauty _____

5. to invite the **socialite** _____

Completing the Sentence

From the words in this Unit, choose the one that best completes each of the following sentences. Write the correct word form in the space provided.

1. Do you believe that the crime rate will go down if the _____ code is made more severe?

2. It is up to you to make good use of the talents with which nature has seen fit to _____ you.

3. When his efforts to _____ off the bill collectors proved unsuccessful, my uncle was forced to declare bankruptcy.

4. Let us hope that scientists are wrong in their _____ predictions that there will be a major earthquake in our region.

5. To carry out his great work, he chose to separate himself from society and live the solitary life of a(n) _____.

6. Some people have the unpleasant habit of verbally _____ their opponents in an argument by loudly repeating a single phrase.

7. Even though you are _____ because the candidate you favored did not win the nomination, you should still vote in the election.

8. In your answers, be precise and try to give only the details that you know are _____ to this investigation.

9. Even before Martin Luther King, Jr., won the Nobel Peace Prize in 1964, his _____ had spread throughout most of the world.

10. In my opinion, the countryside is _____ by billboards that block our view of the beauties of nature.

11. The Scottish poet Robert Burns reminds us that no matter how carefully we plan, things may still go _____.

12. The brave soldiers defending the fort _____ only when they realized that further resistance was useless.

13. We were amazed that the large, fierce-looking dog allowed the child to pull its tail with _____.

14. There's an old saying that tells us that if you walk like a duck and talk like a duck, people are _____ to take you for a duck.

15. As the jurors filed back into the courtroom, their stern _____ alarmed the defendants.

16. The Grand Canyon and Niagara Falls are considered by many to be awe-inspiring _____ of nature.

17. Shoes that will not _____ your feet are the most important piece of equipment you will need for a hike.

18. True, I wanted to make some money, but my _____ reason for taking the job was that I needed practical work experience.

19. The parents promised that they would not meddle with or _____ on the privacy of their married children.

20. We were prepared to make an angry complaint to the salesclerk, but her _____ manner soon put us in a friendlier mood.

Writing: Words in Action

1. Look back at "Tecumseh of the Shawnee" (pages 108–109). Think about what Tecumseh did for his people. Write a tribute to Tecumseh, describing how he positively affected the lives of the Shawnee. Use at least two details from the passage and three Unit words.

2. Think about a leader, past or present, whom you feel has had a positive impact on American society. In a brief essay, describe what this leader has done for the American people and how his or her contributions affect your life today. Support your opinion with specific references to the reading (refer to pages 108–109) or with examples from your own knowledge or experience. Write at least three paragraphs, and use three or more words from this Unit.

Vocabulary in Context
Literary Text

The following excerpts are from Life on the Mississippi *by Mark Twain. Some of the words you have studied in this Unit appear in* **boldface** *type. Complete each statement below the excerpt by circling the letter of the correct answer.*

1. But in speaking of the stage of the river today, at a given point, the captain was pretty **apt** to drop in a little remark about this being the first time he had seen the water so high or so low at that particular point for forty-nine years . . .

    If a person is **apt** to do something, he or she is
    a. afraid to do it   c. enthusiastic about doing it
    b. unlikely to do it   d. very likely to do it

2. We had dinner on a ground-veranda over the water—the chief dish the **renowned** fish called the pompano, delicious as the less criminal forms of sin.

    Food that is **renowned** is definitely NOT
    a. unfamiliar   c. spicy
    b. popular   d. legendary

3. The captain stood around a while in evident discomfort, and once or twice seemed about to make a suggestion; but the etiquette of the river taught him to avoid that sort of rashness, and so he managed to hold his peace. He **chafed** and puzzled a few minutes longer, then retired to his apartments.

    Whenever someone is **chafed**, he is
    a. exhausted   c. aggravated
    b. reflective   d. stubborn

Mark Twain's autobiographical *Life on the Mississippi* has been made into a television movie and a musical.

4. My friend told the medium that when his relative was in this poor world, he was **endowed** with an extraordinary intellect and an absolutely defectless memory . . .

    If something is **endowed** it is
    a. removed   c. managed
    b. granted   d. converted

5. A few more days swept swiftly by, and La Salle stood in the shadow of his confiscating cross, at the meeting of the waters from Delaware, and from Itaska, and from the mountain ranges close upon the Pacific, with the waters of the Gulf of Mexico, his task finished, his **prodigy** achieved.

    A **prodigy** is a
    a. triumph   c. vessel
    b. journey   d. chore

Interactive Quiz

Snap the code, or go to **vocabularyworkshop.com**

Vocabulary for Comprehension

*Read the following passage in which some of the words you have studied in Units 7–9 appear in **boldface** type. Then answer the questions on page 119.*

The following passage discusses the serial novel, a popular literary form that leaves readers eagerly awaiting the next installment.

(Line)

A new literary form known as the *serial novel* developed in England around 1840. It was made famous by Charles Dickens, William
(5)   Makepeace Thackeray, and a number of other writers. The stories were peopled with a lively array of characters, from **unassuming** heroes and **disarming** heroines to
(10)   **predatory** villains. They were faced with realistic and heart-wrenching dilemmas. The story lines were complex, and each episode had a cliff-hanging ending that left readers
(15)   hungry for more.

Serial novels were usually published over a period of a year or more. Each new installment was printed as the author finished it. The
(20)   serial form gave nineteenth-century novelists the freedom to make up their stories as they went along. This allowed them to take the public's reaction into account. Loyal readers
(25)   vigorously **proclaimed** their views in letters to publishers and at open literary discussions.

These writers were not able to **avail** themselves of the kinds of
(30)   sophisticated market research

techniques that today's writers can turn to, but they knew how to satisfy their readers. Depending on the reaction to each new episode, a
(35)   writer might decide to soften a planned harsh ending or provide a long-lost wealthy relative to come to the rescue of a poor character.

The serial novels of Charles
(40)   Dickens were enormously popular, attracting **fervent** fans on both sides of the Atlantic. In Boston, for example, thousands of readers flocked to the harbor to greet the
(45)   ships that brought each new installment from London. The phrase "hot off the press" really meant something to readers eager to know what would become of the
(50)   characters who had won their hearts.

Today's daily soap operas and weekly television series owe much to serial novels. An individual episode stands on its own but is also part of
(55)   an ongoing saga. Viewers and readers regard recurring characters almost as members of the family. They await each new episode to see how the story will unfold.

1. The passage is primarily concerned with
   a. eighteenth-century literature
   b. nineteenth-century serial novels
   c. weekly television series
   d. Charles Dickens's novels
   e. modern soap operas

2. The meaning of **unassuming** (line 8) is
   a. modest
   b. foolish
   c. boastful
   d. friendly
   e. idealistic

3. **Disarming** (line 9) most nearly means
   a. tragic
   b. alarming
   c. flighty
   d. tearful
   e. charming

4. **Predatory** (line 10) is best defined as
   a. comic
   b. snarling
   c. clever
   d. rapacious
   e. proud

5. From the author's description of serial novels (lines 6–15), you can infer that the author
   a. never reads novels
   b. dislikes serial novels
   c. enjoys serial novels
   d. teaches creative writing
   e. is a novelist or playwright

6. Which of the following generalizations would the author agree with?
   a. Authors of serial novels were unmoved by criticism or acclaim.
   b. Serial novels were not popular in America.
   c. Novels in the 1840s were boring.
   d. Charles Dickens is a better novelist than William Makepeace Thackeray.
   e. Authors of serial novels adapted their plots according to readers' responses.

7. The meaning of **proclaimed** (line 25) is
   a. concealed
   b. declared
   c. shouted
   d. changed
   e. repeated

8. **Avail** themselves of (line 29) means
   a. pay for
   b. look up
   c. read about
   d. make use of
   e. put together

9. The function of paragraph 4 (lines 39–50) is to
   a. discuss the modern novel
   b. introduce a totally new topic
   c. dispute the passage's main idea
   d. summarize the passage's main idea
   e. provide a specific example of the main idea

10. **Fervent** (line 41) is best defined as
    a. loyal
    b. stoical
    c. enthusiastic
    d. critical
    e. unconcerned

11. When Dickens was publishing his novels, American readers had to wait until the latest installment arrived by
    a. ship
    b. plane
    c. railroad
    d. computer
    e. telephone

12. The fifth paragraph (lines 51–59) examines the
    a. origins of serial novels
    b. popularity of serial novels
    c. influence of serial novels
    d. plot of a specific novel
    e. structure of a specific novel

Two-Word Completions

Select the pair of words that best completes the meaning of each of the following sentences.

1. The old adage that clothes often _____ the man simply means that a person's _____ is frequently a kind of public statement about his or her personality.
   a. convey . . . renown
   b. attribute . . . mien
   c. defile . . . stance
   d. proclaim . . . attire

2. During the deciding game, the challenger, a 12-year-old _____ by the name of Mikie, _____ the moves of the champion, herself a grand master and chess authority, with the expertise of an accomplished veteran.
   a. prodigy . . . parried
   b. crony . . . belittled
   c. recluse . . . nullified
   d. acme . . . fended off

3. For a while the politician stood high in public favor, but then his reputation suddenly _____ to earth. One day he was basking in the sunshine of popular approval; the next he found himself _____ under the yoke of universal disfavor.
   a. plummeted . . . chafing
   b. wavered . . . encroaching
   c. parried . . . wallowing
   d. belittled . . . rankling

4. At first, I was perfectly content to do the rather _____ tasks that my summer job involved. But as time went on, I became thoroughly _____ with such undemanding and unpleasant assignments.
   a. exotic . . . obsessed
   b. unassuming . . . endowed
   c. menial . . . disgruntled
   d. tawdry . . . intrigued

5. The wolf, a _____ creature that eats large hoofed animals, is often viewed as a threat to ranchers. Presently, the grey wolf has been designated an endangered species, and its most serious threat is human _____ into wolf territory.
   a. fervent . . . impunity
   b. disarming . . . attribution
   c. menial . . . infiltration
   d. predatory . . . encroachment

6. Though they never seem to think alike on any subject, there isn't the slightest hint of _____ between them. I think it's not uncommon for two people whose views _____ so sharply to dislike one another intensely.
   a. juncture . . . abut
   b. enmity . . . diverge
   c. impunity . . . encroach
   d. doctrine . . . nullify

7. Struck by a dreadful disease, my friend became a shadow of her former self. I did not at first recognize the _____ figure that lay in the bed before me. Her once carefree face was now drawn and _____.
   a. cryptic . . . jaunty
   b. ravaged . . . disarming
   c. gaunt . . . haggard
   d. stinted . . . fervent

Proverbs

In the passage about Tecumseh (see pages 108–109), the author makes a statement about the leader, noting that "a true warrior never seeks glory." The author uses this proverb to make the point that real leaders have no desire for glory, especially on the battlefield. They are not motivated by a selfish desire for fame or praise.

A **proverb** is a short saying that summarizes or encapsulates a universal truth. Proverbs often reflect cultural values. Some proverbs are quite old, and their meanings may not be obvious at first. They are best understood in context. Proverbs can be humorous, serious, or insightful, but in all cases they offer sound advice and truths about life.

Choosing the Right Proverb

Read each sentence. Use context clues to figure out the meaning of each proverb in **boldface** *print. Then write the letter of the definition for the proverb in the sentence.*

1. "**Where there's a will, there's a way**," Dad said as we prepared to clean out my closet. _____

2. Don't let the twins stay out after curfew; **if you give them an inch, they'll take a mile**. _____

3. As we watched the former senator's life unravel in the aftermath of the scandal, we realized that **the bigger they are, the harder they fall**. _____

4. When Barry saw that Mike was handing out cookies for votes, he decided to **fight fire with fire** and handed out donuts. _____

5. You have to be able to handle stress if you want to be a manager, so **if you can't stand the heat, get out of the kitchen**. _____

6. Don't be angry at your brother because he forgot your birthday; **let bygones be bygones**. _____

7. Now that Naomi is out of work, she should **make hay while the sun shines** and write her novel. _____

8. I've noticed that complainers often get what they want. I guess it's true that **the squeaky wheel gets the grease**. _____

9. When Lou told me he has refused to play tennis with Henry ever since Henry beat him, I told Lou that he shouldn't **cut off his nose to spite his face**. _____

10. Even though this looks like it will be a bright, sunny day, let's pack our rain parkas. **Hope for the best, but prepare for the worst** is my philosophy. _____

a. If you can't cope with the pressure of a particular task, do something else.

b. Forgive and forget wrongs done to you.

c. When you try to punish someone else, you only punish yourself.

d. Those who plan ahead will not be taken by surprise.

e. If you put your mind to it, you can do anything.

f. Use the same methods as your opponent.

g. Famous, wealthy, or powerful people have more to lose when they fail.

h. The person who is loudest or most persistent will often get what he or she wants.

i. Seize an opportunity.

j. If you are too permissive, people will take advantage of you.

Writing with Proverbs

Find the meaning of each proverb. (Use a dictionary if necessary.) Then write a sentence for each proverb.

1. Leave no stone unturned.

_____

2. Every path has its puddle.

_____

3. Don't spit into the wind.

_____

4. Honesty is the best policy.

_____

5. Tomorrow is a new day.

_____

_____

6. Two's company; three's a crowd.

_____

_____

7. Many a true word is spoken in jest.

_____

_____

8. Few words and many deeds.

_____

9. A rumor goes in one ear and out many mouths.

_____

10. Blood is thicker than water.

_____

11. True beauty lies within.

_____

12. Nothing dries sooner than a tear.

_____

Denotation and Connotation

Every word has a denotation and a connotation. A word's **denotation** is its literal meaning—the way it is defined in a dictionary.

A word's **connotation** is its emotional meaning—the various personal and cultural associations we make with it. Denotations give readers information about the obvious or "surface" meanings of words, while connotations suggest deeper, implied meanings. While denotations are usually neutral in tone, connotations often have strongly positive or negative tones.

Consider these synonyms for the word *determined*.

> unflagging   resolute   pushy   relentless

Unflagging and *resolute* have positive connotations, while *pushy* and *relentless* have negative connotations.

> **Think:** A teammate who is unflagging and resolute can help the group reach its goals, but a teammate who is pushy and relentless will be hard to work with.

Look at these examples of words that are similar in denotation but have different connotations.

NEUTRAL	POSITIVE	NEGATIVE
give	endow	dole
save	economize	stint
thin	slender	gaunt

Good writers understand the power of connotations. If a writer describes a character as *enthusiastic*, the reader imagines someone who is positive and energetic. If a writer describes a character as *fanatical*, however, the reader imagines someone who is obsessed and unstable. Writers choose their words carefully, always keeping these shades of meaning in mind.

Shades of Meaning

Write a plus sign (+) in the box if the word has a positive connotation.
Write a minus sign (–) if the word has a negative connotation. Put a zero (0)
if the word is neutral.

1. renown ☐   **2.** doctrine ☐   **3.** gaunt ☐   **4.** tawdry ☐

5. haggard ☐   **6.** attribute ☐   **7.** jaunty ☐   **8.** acme ☐

9. exotic ☐   **10.** disarming ☐   **11.** proxy ☐   **12.** defile ☐

13. attire ☐   **14.** turncoat ☐   **15.** prodigy ☐   **16.** bludgeoned ☐

Expressing the Connotation

Read each sentence. Select the word in parentheses that better expresses the connotation (positive, negative, or neutral) given at the beginning of the sentence.

positive
1. Candice wrote a(n) (**easy, jaunty**) song that put everyone in a good mood.

positive
2. The young celebrity changed the subject, trying to (**dodge, parry**) a tacky question from the press.

negative
3. The spy assumed a secret identity in order to (**infiltrate, access**) the Allies' intelligence.

negative
4. When our team lost its star player to the flu during the championship game, all of our plans went (**crooked, awry**).

positive
5. Although Diego did not want to take his little brother to the movie, he finally (**capitulated, consented**) out of kindness.

neutral
6. If you use the blender on something other than food, you could (**cancel, nullify**) your warranty.

negative
7. The regime tried to (**remove, excise**) all books that contained controversial ideas.

neutral
8. Most people do not complain when gas prices (**fall, plummet**).

Challenge: Using Connotation

*Choose vocabulary words from Units 7–9 to replace the **boldface** words in the sentences below. Then explain how the connotation of the replacement word changes the tone of the sentence.*

belittled	disgruntled	ravaged
wallowed	stoical	unflagging

1. The publisher **assessed** _____ Nathan's manuscript, stating that his work was absurd.

_____

_____

2. A wildfire that quickly grew out of control completely **destroyed** _____ hundreds of homes as well as a national park.

_____

_____

3. "We would like to offer our **warm** _____ support to those who donated time and money to our local charity."

_____

_____

Classical Roots

chron—time; **cryph,
crypt**—hidden, secret

The Greek root **chron** means "time" The root **cryph** or
crypt appears in **cryptic** (page 100), meaning "puzzling or
mystifying." Some other words based on these roots are
listed below.

anachronism	chronic	chronological	encrypt
apocryphal	crypt	cryptogram	synchronize

*From the list of words above, choose the one that corresponds to each of the brief
definitions below. Write the word in the blank space in the illustrative sentence below
the definition. Use a dictionary if necessary.*

1. of questionable authorship or authenticity, false, counterfeit

Many tales of the exploits of Daniel Boone and Davy Crockett are probably

_____.

2. an underground vault or chamber, often used for burial

Colorful paintings adorned the walls of the pharaoh's _____.

3. something that is out of its proper time

A telephone would be a(n) _____ in a movie set in
colonial times.

4. arranged in the order of time of occurrence

A ship captain's log provides a(n) _____ record of a voyage.

5. to convert a message into a code or cipher

Prisoners sometimes try to _____ pleas for help in
their letters.

6. to occur at the same time

Pairs skaters must _____ their movements so that they
execute their routines in unison.

7. of long duration, continuing; constant

Drought is a(n) _____ problem in many parts of the world.

8. something written in a code to conceal its meaning, a cipher

Army intelligence intercepted an enemy _____.

*Read the following passage, taking note of the **boldface** words and their contexts. These words are among those you will be studying in Unit 10. As you complete the exercises in this Unit, it may help to refer to the way the words are used below.*

The Adventures of Narváez and Cabeza de Vaca in the New World

<Historical Nonfiction>

On June 17, 1527, the Narváez expedition departed from Spain to claim Florida for the Spanish crown. By this time, Spain's **transition** from European kingdom to global empire was well underway. The Spanish were experienced seafarers and colonizers, and by all accounts, the Narváez expedition was **devised** in **accord** with the best practices of the day. The risks **entailed** in such ventures remained high, however. The Narváez expedition was a **veritable** disaster.

Five ships set out that day, carrying 600 men led by the conquistador Pánfilo de Narváez. After three months at sea, the fleet landed on the island of Hispaniola. While the officers procured horses and ships, about 100 men deserted. Weeks later, the expedition arrived at Cuba. At least 80 men, two ships, and many supplies were lost to a hurricane. More bad weather **vexed** the fleet as it sailed around the Cuban coast, and **dexterous** navigation proved no match for the elements.

The battered fleet reached the Florida coast in April 1528, with a crew of about 400 men. They **bartered** with the native villagers, exchanging beads and cloth for food. The villagers must have felt some **trepidation** at the Spaniards' arrival, as they abandoned the village overnight. The Spaniards soon encountered another village, where they heard rumors of gold to the north. Narváez decided to split the party, sending 300 men north by land to **ferret** out the rumored gold, and the rest to sail up the coast. One officer, Alvar Núñez Cabeza de Vaca, argued that it would be wiser to keep the group together. Narváez overruled the dissenter and **upbraided** him with a **curt** reply, accusing him of cowardice. It was a rash decision that the travelers would come to **rue**, but they knew little then of the **impending** challenges.

The 300 men who headed north never saw their ships again. They encountered hospitable villagers who supplied them with food, but they found no cities of gold. Drained of **vitality** by guerilla attacks, food shortages, and disease, the expedition returned south. There, the exhausted men built crude boats, hoping to reach Spanish settlements in Mexico. Most of the men, including Narváez, died during this desperate journey. About 80 men, including Cabeza de Vaca, landed on an island inhabited by the Karankawa tribe, who enslaved the Spaniards. After a harsh winter, only 15 members of the expedition remained. They learned to live among the Karankawa as captive medicine men, practicing the art of healing, moving with their captors between the island and the mainland. When in Rome, do as the Romans do.

Unable to convince the other Spaniards to escape, Cabeza de Vaca set off on his own into the wilderness. He roamed some 150 miles along the coast, making a living as a trader. In the summer of 1532, he encountered three other survivors of the expedition, who were slaves of a local tribe. Cabeza de Vaca joined these men in captivity, and the four planned their escape. Their chance came in the spring of 1535. While their captors were **engrossed** in a feast, the four Spaniards escaped into the desert and headed south for the Rio Grande. Months later, they stumbled upon a party of Spanish slave-hunters, who led them to Mexico City. Nearly nine years after the Narváez expedition had set out from Spain, the journey of these four final survivors had finally reached its end.

Audio

For iWords and audio passages, snap the code, or go to **vocabularyworkshop.com**.

Definitions

Note the spelling, pronunciation, part(s) of speech, and definition(s) of each of the following words. Then write the appropriate form of the word in the blank spaces in the illustrative sentence(s) following. Finally, study the lists of synonyms and antonyms.

1. accord
(ə kôrd′)

(*n.*) agreement, harmony; (*v.*) to agree, be in harmony or bring into harmony; to grant, bestow on

The labor union reached an _____ with management before the midnight deadline.

The Nobel Committee _____ the Peace Prize to the Red Cross in 1917, 1944, and 1963.

SYNONYM: (*n.*) mutual understanding
ANTONYMS: (*n.*) disagreement, conflict, friction

2. barter
(bär′ tər)

(*n.*) an exchange in trade; (*v.*) to exchange goods

By definition, _____ does not involve the exchange of money in any form.

According to the Hebrew Bible, Esau, the brother of Jacob, _____ away his birthright for a hot meal.

SYNONYMS: (*v.*) trade, swap
ANTONYMS: (*v.*) sell, buy, purchase

3. curt
(kərt)

(*adj.*) short, rudely brief

Tour guides are trained to give complete and polite answers to questions, not _____ responses.

SYNONYMS: rude, brusque, terse, summary
ANTONYMS: civil, courteous, lengthy, detailed

4. devise
(di vīz′)

(*v.*) to think out, plan, figure out, invent, create

The advertising agency _____ clever commercials promoting the new car.

SYNONYMS: contrive, work out, design

5. dexterous
(dek′ strəs)

(*adj.*) skillful in the use of hands or body; clever

The _____ movements of those master chefs we see on TV took years of practice to perfect.

SYNONYMS: agile, handy, deft
ANTONYMS: clumsy, awkward, ungainly

6. engross
(en grōs′)

(*v.*) to occupy the complete attention of, absorb fully

The exciting new film _____ every member of the audience.

SYNONYMS: immerse, preoccupy
ANTONYMS: bore, stultify, put to sleep

7. entail
(*v.*, en tāl';
n., en' tāl)

(*v.*) to put a burden on, impose, involve; to restrict ownership of property by limiting inheritance; (*n.*) such a restriction

Reaching your goals will _____ both hard work and sacrifice.

By tradition, an _____ requires that our great-grandmother's paintings must pass to the oldest child.

SYNONYM: (*v.*) necessitate
ANTONYMS: (*v.*) exclude, rule out, preclude

8. ferret
(fcr' ət)

(*n.*) a kind of weasel; (*v.*) to search or hunt out; to torment, badger

_____ were once used to chase rabbits and other pests from their burrows.

No matter how long it takes, we'll keep asking questions until we _____ out the true story.

SYNONYMS: (*v.*) track down, sniff out

9. habituate
(hə bich' ü āt)

(*v.*) to become used to; to cause to become used to

Rookies who quickly _____ themselves to discipline can make important contributions to a team.

SYNONYMS: inure, get used to; ANTONYMS: deprogram, brainwash

10. impending
(im pen' diŋ)

(*adj.*, *part.*) about to happen, hanging over in a menacing way

If you have studied hard, you have no reason to worry about your _____ final exams.

SYNONYMS: imminent, upcoming; ANTONYMS: distant, remote

11. personable
(pərs' nə bəl)

(*adj.*) pleasing in appearance or personality, attractive

A group of very _____ and enthusiastic teens volunteered to help senior citizens with daily chores.

SYNONYMS: agreeable, likable
ANTONYMS: unpleasant, disagreeable

12. rue
(rü)

(*v.*) to regret, be sorry for; (*n.*) a feeling of regret

It is only natural to _____ mistakes and missed opportunities.

My heart was filled with _____ when I realized how thoughtlessly I had behaved.

SYNONYM: (*v.*) repent; ANTONYM: (*v.*) cherish

13. scoff
(skäf)

(*v.*) to make fun of; to show contempt for

People once _____ at the notion that the use of personal computers would become widespread.

SYNONYMS: ridicule, laugh at
ANTONYMS: take seriously, admire, revere

14. transition
(tran zish′ ən)

(*n.*) a change from one state or condition to another

Because of a change in leadership, the country is undergoing a period of political _____.

SYNONYMS: conversion, switch, passage

15. trepidation
(trep ə dā′ shən)

(*n.*) fear, fright, trembling

Even veteran actors experience _____ just before they go on stage.

SYNONYMS: dread, anxiety, apprehension
ANTONYMS: confidence, self-assurance, poise

16. upbraid
(əp brād′)

(*v.*) to blame, scold, find fault with

The police officer _____ the driver for blocking the crosswalk.

SYNONYMS: bawl out, reprimand
ANTONYMS: praise, pat on the back

17. veritable
(ver′ ə tə bəl)

(*adj.*) actual, true, real

Those dusty old boxes in my grandparents' attic contained a _____ treasure trove of rare books and valuable antiques.

ANTONYMS: false, specious

18. vex
(veks)

(*v.*) to annoy, anger, exasperate; to confuse, baffle

The annual task of filling out federal and state income tax returns _____ many people.

SYNONYMS: irritate, irk, puzzle, distress
ANTONYMS: please, delight, soothe, mollify

19. vitality
(vī tal′ ə tē)

(*n.*) strength, energy; the capacity to live and develop; the power to endure or survive

To win a marathon, a runner must have patience, speed, and exceptional _____.

SYNONYMS: verve, stamina
ANTONYMS: lifelessness, torpor, lethargy

20. whimsical
(whim′ zə kəl)

(*adj.*) subject to odd ideas, notions, or fancies; playful; unpredictable

Rube Goldberg was famous for _____ drawings of wildly impractical contraptions.

SYNONYMS: odd, peculiar, quaint, fanciful
ANTONYMS: serious, sober, matter-of-fact, realistic

10

Choosing the Right Word

*Select the **boldface** word that better completes each sentence. You might refer to the passage on pages 126–127 to see how most of these words are used in context.*

1. Rachel Carson hoped her book *Silent Spring* would prompt people to be in (**accord, trepidation**) with her view on the use of insecticides.

2. Millions of people, not only in India but in all parts of the world, came to regard Gandhi as a (**veritable, dexterous**) saint.

3. The mayor warned of a(n) (**whimsical, impending**) crisis unless measures are taken immediately to conserve the city's water supply.

4. When we moved from an apartment to a house, we found that being homeowners (**entails, scoffs**) more responsibilities than we had imagined.

5. A long series of minor illnesses sapped his (**vitality, transition**), leaving him unable to work.

6. Instead of trying to (**rue, devise**) an elaborate excuse, why not tell them exactly what happened and hope for the best?

Rachel Carson's book *Silent Spring*, published in 1962, warned people about the effects of pesticides on the environment.

7. (**Engrossed, Vexed**) in texting, the pedestrian, completely oblivious to his environment, fell right into a manhole.

8. Our science teacher (**engrossed, upbraided**) us when we failed to follow proper safety precautions in the lab.

9. Do not (**scoff, barter**) at him because he wants to be a good student.

10. The years of adolescence mark the (**transition, accord**) from childhood to adulthood.

11. Despite my best efforts, I was unable to (**habituate, ferret**) out the time and place of the meeting.

12. In spite of my (**vitality, trepidation**) about making a speech at the assembly, I found it an enjoyable experience.

13. As the screaming fans stormed the stadium, security prepared for an (**upbraided, impending**) riot.

14. My uncle told me that dropping out of school at an early age was a decision he has always (**rued, ferreted**).

15. You may find it hard to become (**engrossed, upbraided**) in the study of irregular verbs, but you'll have to master them if you want to learn French.

16. My ingenious sister (**engrossed, devised**) a gadget that opens cans, secures nails, and loosens bolts.

17. Although we all long for world peace, we should not allow ourselves to (**entail, barter**) away our liberties to secure it.

18. My cousin is full of (**personable, whimsical**) ideas that may not be practical but are a lot of fun to discuss.

19. The (**vitality, transition**) from country living to city living was more difficult than I imagined.

20. The telegram contained a(n) (**impending, curt**) message ordering me to return home as soon as possible.

21. I wouldn't describe our hostess as merely (**personable, veritable**); I think she is a truly captivating woman.

22. Good office managers must be (**dexterous, curt**) in using their powers to meet goals without discouraging employees.

23. Presidents need capable assistants who will shield them from minor problems that may (**vex, devise**) them.

24. During the oil crisis of the 1970s, Americans had to (**habituate, vex**) themselves to lower indoor temperatures and decreased use of private transportation.

25. Lucinda (**upbraided, bartered**) the fidgety children for their rude behavior.

Synonyms

*Choose the word from this Unit that is the same or most nearly the same in meaning as the **boldface** word or expression in the phrase. Write that word on the line. Use a dictionary if necessary.*

1. thoroughly **acclimated** to harsh winters _____

2. the **changeover** to daylight saving time _____

3. could not have been more **charming** _____

4. **lament** our long separation _____

5. a **quirky** sense of humor _____

6. prepared for the **approaching** deadline _____

7. the surprising **vigor** of a 90-year-old man _____

8. **requires** a thorough knowledge of math _____

9. **teased** out the information _____

10. never **jeered** at my attempts to sing _____

Antonyms

*Choose the word from this Unit that is most nearly opposite in meaning to the **boldface** word or expression in the phrase. Write that word on the line. Use a dictionary if necessary.*

1. a **somber** view of the world　　　　　　　　　_____

2. was **unaccustomed** to the new surroundings　_____

3. **appreciate** your hard work　　　　　　　　　_____

4. an **obnoxious** club member　　　　　　　　　_____

5. never expected such **courteous** treatment　　_____

Completing the Sentence

From the words in this Unit, choose the one that best completes each of the following sentences. Write the correct word form in the space provided.

1. Although I have read *Peter Pan* many times, the _____ characters and imaginative story never fail to amuse me.

2. The project I was working on _____ me so thoroughly that I forgot to stop for lunch.

3. The _____ fingers of the great violinist were guided by his deep understanding of the music.

4. Her early years on her family's farm _____ her to long hours and hard manual labor.

5. I assure you that you will _____ the day you challenged us to a karaoke contest.

6. Since the artist seems to have known everyone of importance in her time, her diaries read like a(n) _____ *Who's Who* of the period.

7. During the twentieth century, many countries in Africa and Asia made the _____ from colonial status to national independence.

8. You should try not to allow petty annoyances to _____ you so much.

9. Before applying for that job, you should know that it _____ late-night and early-morning shifts.

10. During those difficult years, the state was in the hands of a do-nothing administration completely lacking in _____ and direction.

11. Every time I go to the dentist, she _____ me for eating things that are bad for my teeth.

12. I don't expect long explanations, but why must his answers to my questions be so _____ _____?

13. The salesclerk didn't seem to know the stock very well, but he was so pleasant and _____ that we were glad to have him serving us.

14. The firefighters who rescued three families from a burning building fully deserve all the honors _____ them.

15. Before you make fun of my new automatic back scratcher, remember how people _____ at Edison and the Wright brothers.

16. At a well-known theater in Virginia, playgoers could _____ various kinds of food for the price of admission.

17. The purpose of this meeting is to _____ a plan for encouraging recycling in our community.

18. One doesn't have to be a weather specialist to know that a darkening sky is a sign of a(n) _____ storm.

19. It is the job of a gossip columnist to _____ out the "secrets of the stars."

20. When I think of all the things that could go wrong, I view the task ahead with great _____.

Writing: Words in Action

1. Look back at "The Adventures of Narváez and Cabeza de Vaca in the New World" (pages 126–127). Suppose that you are one of the explorers who agrees with Cabeza de Vaca that the group should stay together. Write a letter to Narváez persuading him not to split up the party. Give specific reasons for your request, helping Narváez to understand the probable effects of dividing the group. Use at least two details from the passage and three Unit words.

2. *"I have learned that success is to be measured not so much by the position that one has reached in life as by the obstacles which he has overcome while trying to succeed."*—Booker T. Washington

In a brief essay, explain whether you agree or disagree with Booker T. Washington's statement. First, put Washington's statement in your own words, and explain what the word *success* means to you. Support your opinion with specific examples from the reading (refer to pages 126–27) or from your own observations, experience, or studies. Write at least three paragraphs, and use three or more words from this Unit.

Vocabulary in Context

Literary Text

The following excerpts are from Tarzan of the Apes *by Edgar Rice Burroughs. Some of the words you have studied in this Unit appear in* **boldface** *type. Complete each statement below the excerpt by circling the letter of the correct answer.*

1. In the front room were the three men; the two older deep in argument, while the younger, tilted back against the wall on an improvised stool, was deeply **engrossed** in reading one of Tarzan's books.

Whenever someone is **engrossed**, he or she is

a. riveted   **c.** unconcerned
b. worried   **d.** annoyed

2. As the boats moved slowly over the smooth waters of the bay, Clayton and his wife stood silently watching their departure—in the breasts of both a feeling of **impending** disaster and utter hopelessness.

Feelings or events that are **impending** are NOT

a. forthcoming   **c.** far away
b. life-like   **d.** common

3. He had not in one swift **transition** become a polished gentleman from a savage ape-man, but at last the instincts of the former predominated, and over all was the desire to please the woman he loved, and to appear well in her eyes.

A **transition** is a(n)

a. distraction   **c.** complication
b. alteration   **d.** interruption

4. Professor Porter strove manfully to suppress his own emotions, but the strain upon his nerves and weakened **vitality** were too much for him, and at length, burying his old face in the girl's shoulder, he sobbed quietly like a tired child.

Vitality is

a. exhaustion   **c.** instinct
b. control   **d.** liveliness

Still from the 1932 movie *Tarzan the Ape Man*, the first film in a successful series

5. "Bless me!" exclaimed Mr. Philander, as the car moved off after Clayton. "Who would ever have thought it possible! The last time I saw you, you were a **veritable** wild man, skipping about among the branches of a tropical African forest, and now you are driving me along a Wisconsin road in a French automobile."

If something is **veritable**, it is

a. genuine   **c.** delicate
b. spoiled   **d.** improper

Snap the code, or go to **vocabularyworkshop.com**

*Read the following passage, taking note of the **boldface** words and their contexts. These words are among those you will be studying in Unit 11. As you complete the exercises in this Unit, it may help to refer to the way the words are used below.*

Working Like a Dog
<Interview>

Last month, Working Dog magazine editor Fran Y. DeSoto sat down with dog trainer I. Lee Hsu to find out more about service dogs and therapy dogs.

Interviewer: I. Lee Hsu, you're an animal trainer who works with service dogs and therapy dogs. What is the difference?

Hsu: If you **delve** into it, there are many differences. The **conventional** view is that service dogs are guide dogs for the blind or the hearing impaired, and while that's true, they are also trained to pull wheelchairs, be alert to the sounds of a telephone ringing or a smoke detector beeping, and even retrieve keys or call 911. Service dogs are picked for specific characteristics and temperament. They are not pets; they are working dogs. But that's not to say that a strong, loving

partnership doesn't develop between the dog and the person. The intelligence, kindness, and **gallantry** of these dogs can't be underestimated.

Therapy dogs provide comfort and healing to their owners or to people in hospitals, retirement homes, rehabilitation facilities, or any therapeutic setting. The dogs are brought into a **milieu** where someone needs TLC—tender, loving care—and they are just about the best stress busters around! Therapy dogs are usually pets and don't have the same rigorous training as the service dogs, though they must be well-behaved.

Interviewer: Which breeds make better service dogs or therapy dogs?

Hsu: Labradors and golden retrievers are the most popular choice for service dogs. I'll **cite** a few reasons: They are smart, obedient, confident, hardworking, and highly trainable. Dogs that are too distractible, exuberant, or shy don't make the cut. Therapy dogs come in all types and sizes and can be any breed, as long as they are friendly and respond well to touch and lots of handling.

Interviewer: How does a dog become a service dog?

Hsu: I work with an organization that breeds and trains service dogs, and then matches them with people. The dogs live with a foster family for the first year to socialize them and get them used to being around all types of people and situations. Then a period of intensive training **ensues** before the dogs are paired with a human partner.

Therapy dogs lift the spirits of battle-scarred soldiers.

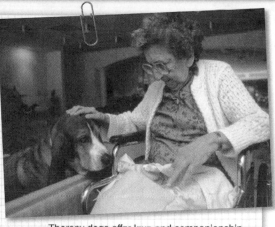
Therapy dogs offer love and companionship to senior citizens.

Interviewer: How do therapy dogs help people?

Hsu: I could **regale** you with heartwarming stories of therapy dogs brought into hospitals to visit sick children or into a home for the elderly or disabled. The dogs are there to be themselves and allow people to pet them. They calm and soothe, lower blood pressure, boost health, and provide much needed affection. They have proven invaluable in **appeasing** kids who have suffered a traumatic event or soldiers who have sustained a **calamitous** injury.

Interviewer: What is a trainer's role?

Hsu: Trainers **impart** their knowledge and experience to both dog and prospective owner. Like humans, dogs have unique traits and **quirks**, and some can be **overbearing** towards other dogs—so we weed out dogs that might cause problems. I have had to **mediate** a few minor scuffles, but nothing too crazy or **outlandish**.

Interviewer: What's your favorite part of the job?

Hsu: It's gratifying to see the young service dogs chow down after a long day of training. There's **judicious** use of rewards, and they have their playtime, too—it's not all work. And it's satisfying to see the positive difference these dogs make in people's lives.

Audio

For iWords and audio passages, snap the code, or go to **vocabularyworkshop.com**.

Service dogs are trained to be in working mode when the vest is on.

Definitions

Note the spelling, pronunciation, part(s) of speech, and definition(s) of each of the following words. Then write the appropriate form of the word in the blank spaces in the illustrative sentence(s) following. Finally, study the lists of synonyms and antonyms.

1. appease
(ə pēz′)

(*v.*) to make calm, soothe; to relieve, satisfy; to yield to

A snack of fresh fruit should _____ your hunger until mealtime.

SYNONYMS: pacify, mollify, propitiate
ANTONYMS: enrage, provoke, irritate

2. belated
(bi lā′ tid)

(*adj.*) late, tardy

The _____ arrival of the party's guest of honor put the hosts in an awkward position.

SYNONYM: behind schedule
ANTONYMS: early, ahead of time

3. calamitous
(kə lam′ it əs)

(*adj.*) causing great misfortune

In 1906, a _____ earthquake and fire leveled much of the city of San Francisco.

SYNONYMS: disastrous, catastrophic, ruinous, fatal
ANTONYMS: fortunate, beneficial, salutary

4. cite
(sīt)

(*v.*) to quote; to mention; to summon to appear in court; to commend, recommend

Be sure to _____ your sources when you write a research paper.

SYNONYMS: refer to, enumerate, subpoena
ANTONYMS: ignore, disregard

5. conventional
(kən ven′ shə nəl)

(*adj.*) in line with accepted ideas or standards; trite

Many people have rather _____ taste in clothing.

SYNONYMS: ordinary, commonplace, orthodox
ANTONYMS: outlandish, bizarre, unorthodox

6. decoy
(*v.*, di koi′;
n., dē′ koi)

(*v.*) to lure into a trap; (*n.*) a person or thing used to lure into a trap

The Pied Piper _____ all the children away from the town of Hamelin by playing his flute.

Painted wooden _____ are prized by collectors of folk art as well as by hunters.

SYNONYMS: (*v.*) entice, entrap; (*n.*) attraction, bait

7. delve
(delv)

(*v.*) to dig; to search deeply and thoroughly into

Scholars continue to _____ into all aspects of America's Civil War.

SYNONYMS: probe, investigate

8. ensue
(en sü′)

(*v.*) to follow in order, come immediately after, and as a result

When an airplane crashes, both investigations and lawsuits can be expected to _____.

SYNONYM: result
ANTONYMS: precede, come before

9. gallantry
(gal′ ən trē)

(*n.*) heroic courage; respect and courtesy; an act or statement marked by a high level of courtesy

The Medal of Honor is awarded by Congress to those who perform acts of "conspicuous _____" in combat.

SYNONYMS: bravery, chivalry, daring
ANTONYMS: cowardice, boorishness

10. impart
(im pärt′)

(*v.*) to make known, tell; to give, pass something on

All over the world, elders _____ the traditions of their culture to younger generations.

SYNONYMS: transmit, bestow, grant
ANTONYMS: withhold, keep back, conceal

11. judicious
(jü dish′ əs)

(*adj.*) using or showing good judgment, wise, sensible

Cautious and _____ people consider all their options before making important decisions.

SYNONYMS: thoughtful, prudent, shrewd, astute
ANTONYMS: foolish, thoughtless, ill-considered

12. mediate
(*v.*, mē′ dē āt;
adj., mē′ dē ət)

(*v.*) to bring about an agreement between persons or groups, act as a go-between; (*adj.*) occupying a middle position; indirect, acting through an intermediary

A neutral third party often _____ contract talks between labor and management.

The name of the _____ star in Orion's Belt is Alnilam.

SYNONYMS: (*v.*) arbitrate, umpire, referee

13. milieu
(mēl yü′)

(*n.*) the setting, surroundings, environment

An authentic _____ is an essential ingredient in a good historical novel.

14. outlandish
(aút land′ ish)

(*adj.*) strange, freakish, weird, foreign-looking; out-of-the-way, geographically remote; exceeding reasonable limits

Imaginative and _____ outfits are popular attire at a costume party.

SYNONYMS: bizarre, odd, unorthodox, unconventional
ANTONYMS: conventional, orthodox, staid, sober

15. overbearing
(ō vər bâr′ iŋ)

(*adj.*) domineering, haughty, bullying; overpowering, predominant

An _____ person has a strong need to be in charge all the time.

SYNONYMS: high-handed, overriding
ANTONYMS: meek, unassuming, self-effacing

16. pert
(pərt)

(*adj.*) high-spirited; lively; bold, saucy; jaunty

Most adults are willing to tolerate a certain amount of _____ behavior in children.

SYNONYMS: vivacious, impudent, fresh
ANTONYMS: sullen, gloomy, peevish

17. quirk
(kwərk)

(*n.*) a peculiar way of acting; a sudden twist or turn

A writer may be famous for creating characters who are full of interesting _____.

SYNONYMS: peculiarity, oddity, eccentricity

18. regale
(ri gāl′)

(*v.*) to feast, entertain agreeably

Most people are eager to _____ their friends with accounts of their vacation adventures.

SYNONYM: divert

19. shiftless
(shift′ ləs)

(*adj.*) lazy, lacking in ambition and energy; inefficient

How can anyone lead a _____ life when there are so many interesting things to learn and to see?

SYNONYMS: careless, sloppy
ANTONYMS: hardworking, ambitious

20. taint
(tānt)

(*n.*) a stain or spot; a mark of corruption or dishonor; (*v.*) to stain or contaminate

The _____ of bribery or other corrupt practices can put an end to the career of a public official.

When toxic chemicals _____ lakes and rivers, many fish and other animals die.

SYNONYMS: (*n.*) blot; (*v.*) soil, tarnished, pollute
ANTONYMS: (*v.*) decontaminate, cleanse

Choosing the Right Word

*Select the **boldface** word that better completes each sentence. You might refer to the passage on pages 136–137 to see how most of these words are used in context.*

1. One of the chief functions of the United Nations is to (**appease, mediate**) disputes between member nations.

2. If you believe a story as (**outlandish, conventional**) as that, I think you would believe anything!

3. Our neighbor came over to (**regale, delve**) us with all the gossip that we had missed during our trip.

4. Though Benedict Arnold originally fought for the American cause, his name is forever (**ensued, tainted**) by his ultimate act of treachery.

5. The best way to (**mediate, impart**) a spirit of patriotism to young people is to teach them about the ideals on which this nation is built.

Jeane Kirkpatrick was America's first female Ambassador to the United Nations.

6. Although some may dismiss "rags-to-riches" stories as silly, I can (**cite, appease**) many examples of wealthy, powerful people who had humble beginnings.

7. Shawn has the most annoying (**quirk, decoy**); he cracks his knuckles loudly just before he turns on his computer.

8. The more I (**regale, delve**) into mythology, the more clearly I see how these ancient stories help us understand the basic truths of life.

9. Language that seems appropriate in the (**milieu, taint**) of the locker room may be totally out of place in the classroom.

10. Although my grandfather did not want to sell his vintage motorcycle, he finally agreed when a collector made him a(n) (**tainted, outlandish**) offer.

11. Foolishly, Neville Chamberlain attempted to avoid a second world war by (**citing, appeasing**) Hitler's demands for territory in Europe.

12. When he finally made (**belated, outlandish**) repayment of the money he owed me, he acted as though he was doing me a big favor.

13. The company has called in an efficiency expert to increase productivity and root out (**judicious, shiftless**) work habits.

14. Whatever his later failures, let us remember that he won the nation's highest military decoration for (**gallantry, decoy**) in action.

15. Although Marge forgot her sister's birthday, she did manage to send her a (**tainted, belated**) birthday card.

16. Helen's physical appearance does not make her stand out, but her high spirits and (**overbearing, pert**) demeanor make her captivating and appealing.

17. Trying to (**regale, appease**) her best friend, Maya agreed to dine at a pizzeria when she really wanted to eat at the new Chinese restaurant.

18. We will not allow ourselves to be (**decoyed, imparted**) into supporting candidates who try to mislead the voters.

19. I am taking this step with my eyes open, and I will accept full responsibility for whatever may (**ensue, impart**).

20. Though some people believe we should make more use of nuclear power, others insist that such a decision would be (**pert, calamitous**).

21. In debate she has the (**overbearing, shiftless**) manner of one who believes firmly that she is never wrong.

22. By careful planning and (**belated, judicious**) investments, Sue greatly increased the fortune that her parents had left her.

23. As every baseball player knows, a knuckleball is extremely hard to hit because its flight is full of unexpected (**quirks, milieus**) called *breaks*.

24. Instead of relying on a (**calamitous, conventional**) textbook, our social studies teacher uses many different materials and media in the classroom.

25. Do you know the proper way to (**cite, ensue**) a source from the Internet?

Synonyms

*Choose the word from this Unit that is the same or most nearly the same in meaning as the **boldface** word or expression in the phrase. Write that word on the line. Use a dictionary if necessary.*

1. raised in an affectionate **atmosphere**   _____

2. a **bouncy** personality   _____

3. cannot explain such **peculiar** behavior   _____

4. a **lackadaisical** approach to studying   _____

5. created a **diversion** to catch the thieves   _____

6. a memorable show of **valor**   _____

7. actions that **ruined** the company's image   _____

8. tried to **settle** arguments between neighbors   _____

9. **amused** us with jokes and silly antics   _____

10. received a **delayed** invitation to the dance   _____

Antonyms

*Choose the word from this Unit that is most nearly opposite in meaning to the **boldface** word or expression in the phrase. Write that word on the line. Use a dictionary if necessary.*

1. looking for **energetic** interns   _____

2. used a pest **repellent**   _____

3. tablets that will **purify** the water   _____

4. thanking you **in advance**   _____

5. possessing a **morose** personality   _____

Completing the Sentence

From the words in this Unit, choose the one that best completes each of the following sentences. Write the correct word form in the space provided.

1. After our bitter quarrel, my brother tried to _____ me by offering to lend me his bicycle.

2. Without trying to _____ deeply into the reasons for their conduct, just briefly describe what they did.

3. He _____ us with food, drink, and endless stories of his seafaring days.

4. Some people will never do the _____ thing when it is possible to behave in an unusual or shocking way.

5. I don't like listening to my older sisters quarrel, so I sometimes step in and attempt to _____ their disagreements.

6. Two of the youngsters acted as _____ while a third tried to swipe a few apples from the unguarded bin.

7. After seven owners had made additions to the house, each in a different style, the building looked so _____ that no one would buy it.

8. Giving up your bus seat to a pretty girl is showing off, but giving it up to a tired senior citizen is true _____.

9. Having grown up in a(n) _____ where children were "seen and not heard," my grandfather is perplexed by the outspoken behavior of today's youth.

10. A good teacher can give you knowledge and skills but cannot _____ the wisdom that comes only with experience.

11. When the American people learned of the bombing of Pearl Harbor in December 1941, they realized that war must _____.

12. After many years of public service, she has a splendid record without the slightest _____ of wrongdoing.

13. "In that smart new outfit, you look as _____ and stylish as a model," I said to my sister.

14. His devil-may-care attitude toward his job eventually earned him a reputation for being _____ and unreliable.

15. We all know that our coach is strict, but can you _____ a single instance in which he has been unfair?

16. A good supervisor is one who can be firm and efficient without giving the impression of being _____.

17. Although I know I should have written long before now, I hope you will accept my _____ thanks for the beautiful gift you sent.

18. When we were upset and confused, it was only your _____ advice that prevented us from doing something foolish.

19. In spite of all that has been reported about pollution, some people still do not grasp its _____ effects on the environment.

20. As my friend became older, the _____ in his behavior grew stranger and more difficult to deal with.

Writing: Words in Action

1. Look back at "Working Like a Dog" (pages 136–137). Think about the various ways in which service dogs are different from family pets. Write a brief essay comparing and contrasting service dogs with family pets. Use at least two details from the passage and three Unit words.

2. Not only dogs, but also monkeys, miniature horses, and some other animals are trained as service animals. Do you think that animals should be trained to help people, or does this kind of training go against the animal's nature? Are there ways in which service animals might benefit from their role as helpers? Write a brief essay in which you support your opinion with evidence from the reading (refer to pages 136–137) or from your own knowledge or experience. Write at least three paragraphs, and use three or more words from this Unit.

Vocabulary in Context
Literary Text

The following excerpts are from Where Angels Fear to Tread *by E.M. Forster. Some of the words you have studied in this Unit appear in* **boldface** *type. Complete each statement below the excerpt by circling the letter of the correct answer.*

1. And Miss Abbott—she, too, was beautiful in her way, for all her gaucheness and **conventionality**. She really cared about life, and tried to live it properly.

   Conventionality is
   a. predictable   c. offensive
   b. uncommon   d. accidental

2. Miss Abbott was equally civil, but not to be **appeased** by good intentions. The child's welfare was a sacred duty to her, not a matter of pride or even of sentiment. By it alone, she felt, could she undo a little of the evil that she had permitted to come into the world.

   Someone who cannot be **appeased** is NOT easily
   a. deceived   c. annoyed
   b. judged   d. soothed

3. He was a tall, weakly-built young man, whose clothes had to be **judiciously** padded on the shoulders in order to make him pass muster. His face was plain rather than not, and there was a curious mixture in it of good and bad.

   If something is done **judiciously**, it is done so
   a. with haste   c. with care
   b. deceitfully   d. clumsily

Still from the 1991 film version of *Where Angels Fear to Tread*

4. A long argument **ensued**, in which the waiter took part, suggesting various solutions. At last Gino triumphed. The bill came to eightpence-halfpenny, and a halfpenny for the waiter brought it up to ninepence. Then there was a shower of gratitude on one side and of deprecation on the other . . .

   If an argument has **ensued**, it has
   a. ended   c. delivered
   b. developed   d. paused

5. For the barrier of language is sometimes a blessed barrier, which only lets pass what is good. Or—to put the thing less cynically—we may be better in new clean words, which have never been **tainted** by our pettiness or vice.

   If something is **tainted**, it has been
   a. sullied   c. pointed out
   b. uttered   d. sidetracked

Snap the code, or go to **vocabularyworkshop.com**

*Read the following passage, taking note of the **boldface** words and their contexts. These words are among those you will be studying in Unit 12. As you complete the exercises in this Unit, it may help to refer to the way the words are used below.*

To the Bat Cave!
<Informational Essay>

One day in the late 1800s, while riding near New Mexico's Carlsbad Caverns, cowboy Jim White thought he saw smoke plumes rising in the distance. On closer approach, however, he found that this impression was a **fallacy**. What he had really glimpsed was a cloud of bats emerging from the entrance to a **capacious** cave.

The Carlsbad Caverns house thousands of Mexican free-tailed bats.

It was a **pivotal** moment that changed the history of Carlsbad Caverns. For millions of years, this spectacular underground formation was known only to a sprinkling of Paleo-Indians and to a millionfold colony of bats. Now the caverns would be the **recipient** of world-class scientific investigation and the attention of countless tourists.

The subterranean geological wonders of Carlsbad Caverns are impressive, but it is the bats that grab everyone's attention. From April to October, the cavern ceilings **teem** with hundreds of thousands of Mexican free-tailed bats (*Tadarida brasiliensis*). The cave is a maternity roost where the bats bear and rear their young. The total darkness of the cave is a refuge

The bats of Carlsbad Caverns emerge from their caves each night.

for the bats from predators and from people. For centuries, bats have been the victims of countless myths and **caustic** criticism. These false **tenets** are a Pandora's box for those creatures, engendering hatred and fear that has caused humans to mistreat and misunderstand bats for centuries. For people who like bats, a view of thousands upon thousands of bats flying out of the mouth of the cavern for a night of hunting is not to be missed.

Their flight may appear erratic or even **ungainly**. But nature has **bestowed** on bats one of the most sophisticated guidance systems known to science. Mexican freetails, like most bats, use echolocation to navigate and to locate their prey. The bats send out ultrahigh frequency sounds, similar to those emitted by dolphins and whales. When these signals strike an object, their reflections enable the bat to pinpoint the object and fly accordingly. This process occurs in a fraction of a second. Echolocation ensures that practically no **ruse** or evasive action will allow a bat's targeted prey to escape.

A Mexican freetail's **voracious** appetite is one of the bat's prime gifts to humanity. On its nightly flights, one bat may gorge on half its weight in prey. They eat mosquitoes, moths, and other night-flying insects. The bats of Carlsbad Caverns are small. They weigh in at four to five ounces and have a twelve-inch wingspan. But experts estimate that these diminutive creatures dispose of more than one

million pounds of insects annually. Without the bats, the corn and cotton growers in the region would find their agricultural pest problems far less **tractable**. In addition to helping farmers with insect control, bats also provide fertilizer in the form of guano, or droppings. Bat guano was mined for some years after the discovery of the caverns. Mining guano might seem gross or **nauseating**, but it was highly profitable. Guano mining is no longer allowed, as it disturbs the stunning cave environment and the bats.

Nowadays, Carlsbad Caverns is recognized as a unique national treasure. Preservation groups organize **crusades** to maintain the pristine beauty of the caves and to ensure that tourists do not **deface** the rock formations. Meanwhile, the bats inhabit the caves as they have for millennia.

Audio

For iWords and audio passages, snap the code, or go to **vocabularyworkshop.com**.

Definitions

Note the spelling, pronunciation, part(s) of speech, and definition(s) of each of the following words. Then write the appropriate form of the word in the blank spaces in the illustrative sentence(s) following. Finally, study the lists of synonyms and antonyms.

1. abdicate
(ab' də kāt)

(*v.*) to resign, formally give up an office or a duty; to disown, discard

Of all England's monarchs, Edward VIII was the only one to _____ the throne voluntarily.

SYNONYMS: relinquish, renounce
ANTONYM: retain

2. bestow
(bi stō')

(*v.*) to give as a gift; to provide with lodgings

The nation will _____ its highest civilian honor on the noted educator.

SYNONYMS: confer, lodge, put up
ANTONYMS: receive, take, take back, take away

3. capacious
(kə pā' shəs)

(*adj.*) able to hold much, roomy

Whenever I go beach-combing, I take along a backpack with _____ compartments and pockets.

SYNONYMS: spacious, commodious
ANTONYMS: cramped, confined, restricted, narrow

4. caustic
(kô' stik)

(*adj.*) able to burn or eat away by chemical action; biting, sarcastic

All _____ household liquids, such as drain cleaners, must be kept out of the reach of children.

SYNONYMS: burning, corrosive, sharp
ANTONYMS: bland, mild, sugary, saccharine

5. crusade
(krü sād')

(*n.*) a strong movement to advance a cause or idea; (*v.*) to campaign, work vigorously

Rachel Carson's landmark book *Silent Spring* sparked the _____ to ban the use of DDT.

The people who _____ for civil rights in America during the 1960s came from all walks of life.

SYNONYMS: (*n.*) campaign, organized movement

6. deface
(di fās')

(*v.*) to injure or destroy the surface or appearance of; to damage the value, influence, or effect of; to face down, outshine

In many towns, those who _____ walls with graffiti must pay a fine and clean up the mess.

SYNONYMS: mar, disfigure
ANTONYMS: repair, restore, renovate, recondition

7. embargo
(em bär′ gō)

(*n.*) an order forbidding the trade in or movement of commercial goods; any restraint or hindrance; (*v.*) to forbid to enter or leave port; to forbid trade with

The U.S. Congress may impose an _____ against a country that violates trade agreements.

In wartime, the president may _____ goods from countries that trade with the nation's enemies.

SYNONYMS: (*n.*) stoppage, boycott

8. fallacy
(fal′ ə sē)

(*n.*) a false notion or belief; an error in thinking

Reviewers cited several major _____ in the controversial author's newest book.

SYNONYM: misconception; ANTONYMS: sound reasoning, logic

9. levity
(lev′ ə tē)

(*n.*) a lack of seriousness or earnestness, especially about things that should be treated with respect; buoyancy, lightness in weight

A bit of _____ may help you to cope with difficult people or situations.

SYNONYMS: giddiness, flippancy, frivolity, fickleness
ANTONYMS: humorlessness, solemnity

10. mendicant
(men′ də kənt)

(*n.*) beggar; (*adj.*) depending on begging for a living

People who have fallen on hard times may have no choice but to become _____.

_____ friars roamed the streets of medieval towns and cities, asking for coins.

SYNONYM: (*n.*) panhandler
ANTONYMS: (*n.*) millionaire, philanthropist

11. nauseate
(nô′ zē āt)

(*v.*) to make sick to the stomach; to fill with disgust

The fumes that _____ everyone in the building were traced to a faulty heating system.

SYNONYMS: sicken, disgust; ANTONYMS: delight, tickle pink

12. negate
(ni gāt′)

(*v.*) to nullify, deny, bring to nothing

One offensive remark may well _____ the goodwill a politician has built up among voters.

SYNONYMS: invalidate, annul
ANTONYMS: aver, corroborate, buttress

13. pivotal
(piv′ ət əl)

(*adj.*) vitally important, essential

The D-Day invasion was _____ to the Allies' eventual victory in Europe in World War II.

SYNONYMS: crucial, critical, decisive, seminal
ANTONYMS: unimportant, insignificant

14. recipient
(ri sip′ ē ənt)

(*n.*) one who receives; (*adj.*) receiving; able or willing to receive

The first American _____ of the Nobel Prize for literature was the novelist Sinclair Lewis.

A long list of _____ charities may benefit from a wealthy individual's generosity.

SYNONYMS: (*n.*) receiver, beneficiary
ANTONYMS: (*n.*) donor, benefactor, contributor

15. ruse
(rüz)

(*n.*) an action designed to confuse or mislead, a trick

Thieves employ a variety of _____ to gain entrance to homes and apartments.

SYNONYMS: stratagem, subterfuge, dodge

16. teem
(tēm)

(*v.*) to become filled to overflowing; to be present in large quantities

Our national parks _____ with visitors during the summer months.

SYNONYMS: abound, swarm, overflow
ANTONYMS: lack, be wanting

17. tenet
(ten′ ət)

(*n.*) an opinion, belief, or principle held to be true

One of the primary _____ of medicine is to do no harm to the sick and injured.

SYNONYMS: doctrine, precept

18. tractable
(trak′ tə bəl)

(*adj.*) easily managed, easy to deal with; easily wrought, malleable

A _____ colleague is preferable to one who is unwilling to cooperate or compromise.

SYNONYMS: submissive, docile, yielding, amenable
ANTONYMS: unruly, obstreperous, refractory

19. ungainly
(ən gān′ lē)

(*adj.*) clumsy, awkward; unwieldy

The first time I tried to ice-skate, my movements were hesitant and _____.

SYNONYM: graceless
ANTONYMS: nimble, agile, supple, graceful

20. voracious
(vô rā′ shəs)

(*adj.*) having a huge appetite, greedy, ravenous; excessively eager

Newly hatched caterpillars are _____ eaters of leafy green plants.

SYNONYMS: gluttonous, insatiable, avid
ANTONYMS: indifferent, apathetic

Shakespeare's

Choosing the Right Word

Select the **boldface** word that better completes each sentence. You might refer to the passage on pages 146–147 to see how most of these words are used in context.

1. Although the play is titled *Julius Caesar*, I think that the (**pivotal**, **ungainly**) character, on whom all the action depends, is Mark Antony.

2. The Slam-Dunk Giveaway will send one lucky (**recipient**, **mendicant**) on a paid vacation for two to lovely Hawaii.

3. The fact that she is not a member of the Board of Education does not (**negate**, **abdicate**) her criticisms of the school system.

4. His mind is closed, as though he had placed a(n) (**embargo**, **crusade**) on new ideas.

Shakespeare's play *Julius Caesar* is based on historical events that occurred in Rome in 44 BCE.

5. I am willing to become a veritable (**recipient**, **mendicant**) in order to raise money for that most worthy cause.

6. It's good to be open to new ideas, but don't become so (**mendicant**, **tractable**) that you have no firm opinions of your own.

7. When the United States gives out foreign aid, are the (**recipient**, **pivotal**) nations supposed to make repayment?

8. It is a (**fallacy**, **tenet**) to say that because no human being has ever traveled to Mars, no human being ever will.

9. We will not allow you to (**embargo**, **abdicate**) your responsibilities as a leading citizen of this community.

10. She is a very severe critic, and the (**capacious**, **caustic**) comments in her reviews have made her many enemies.

11. With such a (**pivotal**, **voracious**) appetite, the meat-eating dinosaur T. Rex was a horrifying hunter and scavenger.

12. As soon as the new highway extension was built, the sleepy town began to (**teem**, **bestow**) with activity.

13. A favorite bedtime (**tenet**, **ruse**) of small children is to keep asking for a glass of water to delay having to go to sleep.

14. One of the (**tenets**, **fallacies**) of modern art is to experiment with forms, materials, and processes to create new ways of looking at everyday objects.

15. I can forgive most human weaknesses, but I am (**nauseated**, **defaced**) by hypocrisy.

16. "All that I have to (**negate, bestow**) on you," said the elderly father to his son, "is an honorable family name."

17. Instead of launching a great (**crusade, fallacy**) to save the world, why not try to help a few people in your own neighborhood?

18. She has a (**capacious, tractable**) mind that seems able to hold endless information and ideas on any subject.

19. Although the students made jokes about the coming exams, we knew that beneath the (**ruse, levity**) they were quite worried.

20. Weather and pollution had so (**defaced, nauseated**) the statue that its original expression was no longer distinguishable.

21. The four-foot waves made the boat pitch up and down, causing many passengers to become (**capacious, nauseated**).

22. Has anyone ever measured how many hours of TV time are needed to satisfy a small child's (**tractable, voracious**) appetite for cartoons?

23. One guiding (**tenet, levity**) of our energy program is that it is just as important to avoid wasting energy as it is to increase its production.

24. The tall boy who appeared so (**caustic, ungainly**) as he walked through the school corridors was agile and coordinated on the basketball court.

25. (**Voracious, Caustic**) fumes can produce injuries to eyes, skins, and lungs.

Synonyms

*Choose the word from this Unit that is the same or most nearly the same in meaning as the **boldface** word or expression in the phrase. Write that word on the line. Use a dictionary if necessary.*

1. forced to **step down**　　　　　　　　　　_____

2. acts of cruelty that **repulsed** us all　　　_____

3. possesses a **cutting** wit　　　　　　　　_____

4. the **battle** to end poverty　　　　　　　　_____

5. had good reason to **cancel** the agreement　_____

6. a group of ragged **paupers**　　　　　　　_____

7. **bans** on counterfeit designer goods　　　　_____

8. set up a **scam** to fool the police　　　　　_____

9. a theory based entirely on **bogus ideas**　　_____

10. providing some **humor** for the weary soldiers _____

Antonyms

*Choose the word from this Unit that is most nearly opposite in meaning to the **boldface** word or expression in the phrase. Write that word on the line. Use a dictionary if necessary.*

1. surprised by the **seriousness** of your remarks _____

2. forcefully **claimed** the throne _____

3. patiently **confirmed** his remarks _____

4. allowing **free trade** among countries _____

5. scholarships offered by a **wealthy** person _____

Completing the Sentence

From the words in this Unit, choose the one that best completes each of the following sentences. Write the correct word form in the space provided.

1. Though a number of people may be nominated for the best actress Oscar each year, only one of them will be the actual _____ of it.

2. If any of the _____ substance gets on your clothing, wash it off with lukewarm water to prevent it from eating away the fabric.

3. I suspect that he visits the wealthy widow at the nursing home mainly because he thinks she will _____ part of her fortune on him in gratitude.

4. The horse was often hard to manage, but he was _____ as long as he was headed in the direction of the barn.

5. She is such a(n) _____ reader that she often has a book propped up in front of her while she is eating.

6. The president placed a(n) _____ on the sale of arms to the two nations at war.

7. In the early decades of the twentieth century, reform-minded journalists called *muckrakers* _____ vigorously against corruption in government.

8. When he realized that he had completely lost the loyalty and support of his people, the ruler of the small nation chose to _____ and live in exile.

9. For thousands of years, thoughtless tourists have _____ monuments of the past by writing or carving their initials on them.

10. Your attempts at _____ during the most serious moments of the dedication ceremony were decidedly out of place.

11. I have never seen a car with a trunk _____ enough to hold all the luggage you want to take on any trip.

12. The noise in the crowded train station gave me a headache, and the foul odor _____ me.

13. Whenever I pass a group of homeless _____ huddled in a doorway, I give them my spare change.

14. San Francisco is a city that _____ with color and places of historical interest.

15. Since the Greeks could not capture Troy by force, they resorted to the now-legendary _____ of the wooden horse to take the city.

16. Although seals and sea lions are _____ on land, they are extremely graceful in the water.

17. Dad said that he was enjoying the fig-banana pie I had concocted, but the funny look on his face _____ his words.

18. It was not hard for Ted's opponents to shoot holes in his argument, since the _____ it contained were as clear as day.

19. Our victory over South High was the _____ game of the season because it gave us the self-confidence we needed to win the championship.

20. A fundamental _____ of democracy is that all people are equal before the law.

Writing: Words in Action

1. Look back at "To the Bat Cave!" (pages 146–147). Suppose you are a magazine writer in the early 1900s, when Carlsbad Caverns became a national monument. You have been asked to write an article to attract visitors to the caves. Write your article, persuading readers that Carlsbad Caverns is a "geological wonder" and that the nightly bat flights should not be missed. Use at least two details from the passage and three Unit words.

2. The author of "To the Bat Cave!" mentions that bats have been the victims of myths and criticism. What are some of these myths? Why do you think bats have such a negative reputation? Do you think places such as Carlsbad Caverns can help change these misconceptions? Write a brief essay, supporting your ideas with evidence from the reading (refer to pages 146–147) or from your own knowledge or experience. Write at least three paragraphs, and use three or more words from this Unit.

Vocabulary in Context

Literary Text

The following excerpts are from The Lost World *by Sir Arthur Conan Doyle. Some of the words you have studied in this Unit appear in* **boldface** *type. Complete each statement below the excerpt by circling the letter of the correct answer.*

1. Scraps of popular songs were chorused with an enthusiasm which was a strange prelude to a scientific lecture, and there was already a tendency to personal chaff which promised a jovial evening to others, however embarrassing it might be to the **recipients** of these dubious honors.

Recipients are those who

a. donate
b. receive
c. appoint
d. entertain

2. For a moment I wondered where I could have seen that **ungainly** shape, that arched back with triangular fringes along it, that strange bird-like head held close to the ground. Then it came back, to me. It was the stegosaurus . . .

Something **ungainly** is

a. bizarre
b. detailed
c. lumbering
d. visible

3 the Professor stood with one hand raised and his enormous head nodding sympathetically, as if he were **bestowing** a pontifical blessing upon the crowd . . .

The act of **bestowing** involves

a. granting
b. resigning
c. scattering
d. banning

Scene from the 1925 film *The Lost World*, which used stop-motion animation techniques to create dinosaurs that seemed realistic.

4. ". . . As to the small **ruse** which I played upon you in the matter of the envelope, it is clear that, had I told you all my intentions, I should have been forced to resist unwelcome pressure to travel out with you."

A **ruse** is a(n)

a. concern
b. explanation
c. objective
d. deception

5. "Suppose," he cried with feeble violence, "that all the debts in the world were called up simultaneously . . . what . . . would happen then?"

I gave the self-evident answer that I should be a ruined man, upon which he jumped from his chair, [and] reproved me for my habitual **levity** . . .

A person who possesses **levity** is NOT

a. serious
b. humorous
c. light-hearted
d. intelligent

Snap the code, or go to **vocabularyworkshop.com**

Vocabulary for Comprehension

*Read the following passage in which some of the words you have studied in Units 10–12 appear in **boldface** type. Then answer the questions on page 157.*

In this passage, you will learn about Kabuki, a unique form of Japanese theater.

(Line)

About 400 years ago, a spectacular type of theater developed in the ancient Japanese capital city of Kyoto. It is called

(5) *Kabuki*, from the words *ka*, which means "song"; *bu*, which means "dance"; and *ki*, which means "skill." Kabuki actors must excel in all these arts. They undergo many years of

(10) rigorous training that usually begins when they are small children.

Over the centuries, Kabuki has developed into a highly stylized art form that **regales** audiences with an

(15) exciting blend of song, dance, speech, and mime. With its gorgeous costumes and spectacular stage effects, Kabuki is a **veritable** feast for the eyes and ears.

(20) The inventor of Kabuki was a shrine attendant named Okuni. She began by performing her plays, which were based on Buddhist themes, in Kyoto's dry riverbeds.

(25) Okuni recruited other women performers, and their dance plays quickly became very popular. However, the government considered it improper for women to

(30) take part in theatrical performances. In 1629, it banned women from the stage. Since then, the performers in Kabuki have all been men.

Kabuki was the first Japanese

(35) theater art that was designed to appeal to the common people, rather than the royal court or the warrior class (the samurai). As the merchant class and farmers grew

(40) more prosperous during the seventeenth century, Kabuki's popularity increased.

The plays performed by Kabuki troupes include historical sagas, love

(45) stories, ghost stories, and tales of domestic tragedy. Comic interludes that portray the foolish **quirks** of human nature are interspersed to add a note of **levity** to the program.

(50) And while the plays are intended to entertain, they also **impart** moral lessons. The virtuous are rewarded, and the wicked are punished.

Though Kabuki is hundreds of

(55) years old, it is not a dusty relic. It retains tremendous **vitality** and continues to delight audiences wherever it is performed.

1. The main purpose of the passage is to
   a. describe a typical Kabuki play
   b. give a brief history of Kabuki
   c. explain the cultural history of Japan
   d. give a brief biography of Okuni
   e. describe the author's experiences in Japan

2. The etymology of the word *Kabuki* (lines 4–7) suggests that this art form
   a. is performed mainly for children
   b. originated in ancient Greek drama
   c. is performed by amateur actors
   d. is an ancient African ritual
   e. is based on music and dance

3. The meaning of **regales** (line 14) is
   a. annoys
   b. pacifies
   c. bores
   d. entertains
   e. instructs

4. Veritable (line 18) most nearly means
   a. true
   b. meager
   c. tawdry
   d. specious
   e. enjoyable

5. From words like *gorgeous* and *spectacular* in paragraph 2, you can infer that the author's attitude toward Kabuki can best be described as
   a. ironic
   b. admiring
   c. critical
   d. disinterested
   e. analytical

6. Why are all Kabuki performers men?
   a. Kabuki performances are too athletic for women.
   b. Kabuki scripts call for male actors only.
   c. The Japanese government banned women from the stage.
   d. The inventor of Kabuki was a man.
   e. Members of the royal court preferred male performers.

7. One of the reasons for the early popularity of Kabuki is that it
   a. was created by the samurai
   b. dealt with patriotic themes
   c. was seen only by royalty
   d. was completely without humor
   e. appealed to the common people

8. Quirks (line 47) is best defined as
   a. oddities
   b. fantasies
   c. mistakes
   d. sorrows
   e. faults

9. The meaning of **levity** (line 49) is
   a. pity
   b. sanity
   c. piety
   d. frivolity
   e. solemnity

10. Impart (line 51) most nearly means
   a. ignore
   b. repeat
   c. conceal
   d. criticize
   e. transmit

11. Vitality (line 56) is best defined as
   a. importance
   b. timeliness
   c. liveliness
   d. seriousness
   e. appropriateness

12. According to the final paragraph (lines 54–58), Kabuki is
   a. a dying form of theater
   b. still being performed today
   c. no longer being performed
   d. the author's favorite pastime
   e. no longer popular in Japan

Two-Word Completions

Select the pair of words that best completes the meaning of each of the following sentences.

1. Despite the _____ of a few brave men, whose daring deeds on that fateful day are still remembered by history, imperial Rome suffered a(n) _____ defeat that brought a once-mighty empire to its knees.
   a. trepidation . . . veritable
   b. gallantry . . . calamitous
   c. vitality . . . whimsical
   d. dexterity . . . impending

2. "Though I'd spent all my life in a rural environment, I didn't think I'd have any trouble adjusting to city life," Ted said to his friend. "But making the _____ to an urban _____ proved to be much more difficult than I had ever imagined."
   a. crusade . . . recipient
   b. tenet . . . embargo
   c. transition . . . milieu
   d. ruse . . . tenet

3. Long overdue though it surely was, his _____ apology was sufficient to _____ my anger and soothe my hurt feelings.
   a. belated . . . appease
   b. dexterous . . . vex
   c. curt . . . negate
   d. caustic . . . mediate

4. "I feel well prepared and don't view the upcoming scholarship examination with any _____," I asserted confidently. "Still, it's a serious matter, and I'm not treating it with undue _____ either."
   a. gallantry . . . vitality
   b. nausea . . . dexterity
   c. curtness . . . vexation
   d. trepidation . . . levity

5. The speaker did not _____ many examples to back up her argument, but those that she did provide were extremely well chosen. A larger but less _____ selection of illustrations probably would not have made such a powerful impression on the audience.
   a. devise . . . ungainly
   b. impart . . . outlandish
   c. cite . . . judicious
   d. bestow . . . capacious

6. "My ability to hold on to this job will depend on the answer to one _____ question," I thought. "Will I prove to be truly hardworking and reliable, or _____ and irresponsible?"
   a. pivotal . . . shiftless
   b. whimsical . . . personable
   c. impending . . . tractable
   d. caustic . . . dexterous

7. "That rock group's strange antics, _____ costumes, and weird songs don't really impress me," Clara remarked. "Frankly, I prefer musicians who are much more _____."
   a. caustic . . . whimsical
   b. pert . . . overbearing
   c. bartered . . . tainted
   d. outlandish . . . conventional

Idioms

In the passage "Working Like a Dog" (see pages 136–137), the trainer tells the interviewer that he enjoys watching the dogs "chow down" after a long day of training. "Chow down" is an idiom that means "to eat something quickly and hungrily."

Idioms are words, phrases, or sayings whose meanings are figurative, not literal. When you hear a new idiom, think about the context in which it is used. Consider how the literal meaning might point to a more abstract meaning. Listen also to the speaker's tone: Is the idiom playful, critical, or matter-of-fact?

Choosing the Right Idiom

*Read each sentence. Use context clues to figure out the meaning of each idiom in **boldface** print. Then write the letter of the definition for the idiom in the sentence.*

1. My brother has Friday off, but I'll be heading **back to the salt mines**. _____

2. Although the defendant was guilty, all he got was **a slap on the wrist**. _____

3. It doesn't matter whether the traffic accident was caused by speeding or by carelessness; **it amounts to the same thing**. _____

4. Kim buys cookies at the corner bakery because they always pack **a baker's dozen**. _____

5. Andrew thinks a successful salesperson has to **come on strong** to customers, but I disagree. _____

6. Getting a window office was the **icing on the cake** after I got my promotion and pay raise. _____

7. Don't tease Jasmine about falling off the horse yesterday; you'll just **rub salt in the wound**. _____

8. Grace **made no bones about** her decision to vote for Judge Lowden. _____

9. Todd **got off on the wrong foot** with his supervisor, but later he impressed her with a great idea. _____

10. Miguel was **on pins and needles** waiting for the result of his math exam. _____

a. act aggressively and forcefully

b. make something painful even worse

c. a mild punishment

d. thirteen

e. an extra benefit on top of something that's already good

f. started off poorly

g. anxious or nervous

h. back to work

i. was clear and direct about

j. the outcome is the same either way

Writing with Idioms

Find the meaning of each idiom. (Use a dictionary if necessary.) Then write a sentence for each idiom.

1. wing it

_____

2. rule of thumb

_____

3. pipe down

_____

4. on the same page

_____

5. tighten the reins

_____

_____

6. cold feet

_____

_____

7. chicken out

_____

_____

8. green around the gills

_____

9. switch over to

_____

10. ruffle someone's feathers

_____

11. in a nutshell

_____

12. a red herring

_____

Denotation and Connotation

When you are determining the meaning of a word, it's important to consider both its denotation and its connotation. The **denotation** is the word's definition, its literal meaning as presented in a dictionary. The denotation is stated in an objective, logical way.

The **connotation** of a word is its emotional impact. Some words give rise to positive feelings, while others give rise to negative feelings. Words that evoke mild feelings, or none at all, are said to be neutral.

Consider these synonyms for the neutral word *short*.

> *concise*   *crisp*   *curt*   *terse*

Concise and *crisp* have positive connotations, whereas *curt* and *terse* are negative.

> **Think:** In an interview, crisp and concise responses are professional, while curt or terse responses are rude.

Look at these examples. Notice the different connotations of words with similar denotations.

NEUTRAL	POSITIVE	NEGATIVE
large	capacious	baggy
undo	reverse	negate
plan	devise	scheme

Whether you're writing or speaking, make sure the words you choose have the appropriate connotations. For example, describing a friend as *sloppy* would evoke negative feelings, while describing that same friend as *casual* would evoke more positive feelings. Always think carefully about the possible impact a particular word may have on different audiences before you choose one word over another.

Shades of Meaning

Write a plus sign (+) in the box if the word has a positive connotation.
Write a minus sign (–) if the word has a negative connotation. Put a zero (0)
if the word is neutral.

1. cite ☐   **2.** personable ☐   **3.** deface ☐   **4.** fallacy ☐

5. scoff ☐   **6.** caustic ☐   **7.** recipient ☐   **8.** nauseate ☐

9. dexterous ☐   **10.** upbraid ☐   **11.** negate ☐   **12.** gallantry ☐

13. calamitous ☐   **14.** pert ☐   **15.** ungainly ☐   **16.** bestow ☐

WORD STUDY

Expressing the Connotation

Read each sentence. Select the word in parentheses that better expresses the connotation (positive, negative, or neutral) given at the beginning of the sentence.

negative   **1.** Her coaching style is (**forceful, overbearing**) but effective.

neutral   **2.** Please do not (**taint, alter**) the delicate flavor of the soup with another tablespoon of salt.

negative   **3.** Several countries agreed to impose a(n) (**prohibition, embargo**) on the sale of arms to a rogue government.

positive   **4.** The beach was (**teeming, swarming**) with seagulls and turtles.

neutral   **5.** When you consider his many (**quirks, habits**), you must agree that whistling is the least annoying of them all.

positive   **6.** Our new puppy has a (**voracious, gluttonous**) appetite and should soon grow into a strong and healthy dog.

positive   **7.** My mother likes to decorate our yard with wind chimes, statues of gnomes, and other (**odd, whimsical**) garden décor.

negative   **8.** Pierre, the so-called writer, claims he has had writer's block for months, but I think he is just (**shiftless, laid-back**).

Challenge: Using Connotation

*Choose vocabulary words from Units 10–12 to replace the **boldface** words in the sentences below. Then explain how the connotation of the replacement word changes the tone of the sentence.*

outlandish	vexed	scoffed
appeased	nauseated	judicious

1. Everyone loves to watch the performers on the red carpet and critique their **unusual** _____ attire.

_____

_____

2. Can you believe there was a time when people **laughed** _____ at the idea that women had a right to vote?

_____

_____

3. Airplane turbulence, strong chemical fumes, and super-fast thrill rides all make me feel **bad** _____.

_____

_____

Classical Roots

ven, vent—to come

This Latin root appears in **conventional** (page 138). Literally, the word means "referring to or resulting from a coming together." It now has the meaning "customary, common, expected, lacking in originality." Some other words in which this root appears are listed below.

circumvent	eventful	intervene	revenue
convene	eventual	inventive	venue

From the list of words above, choose the one that corresponds to each of the brief definitions below. Write the word in the blank space in the illustrative sentence below the definition. Use a dictionary if necessary.

1. the place where a crime or cause of legal action occurs; a locality from which a jury is called and in which a trial is held; the scene or locale of any action or event

A defense attorney may sometimes request a change of _____ in order to assure a client a fair trial.

2. to assemble, come together; to call together

The new book discussion group plans to _____ once a month.

3. good at making or thinking up new ideas or things; imaginative

The notebooks of Leonardo da Vinci contain abundant evidence of his remarkably inquisitive and _____ intellect.

4. to come between; to enter to help settle a dispute

I refuse to _____ in their argument because I do not want to take sides.

5. happening at an unspecified time in the future, ultimate

If you stick to an exercise program, you will see _____ improvement in your strength and fitness.

6. income; the income of a government; the yield from property or investment

_____ from the new product line has exceeded the company's expectations.

7. to get around or avoid; to defeat, overcome

The pilot was able to _____ the storm by flying farther west.

8. full of events or incidents; important

Someone who has led a very _____ life may decide to write an autobiography.

Read the following passage, taking note of the **boldface** words and their contexts. These words are among those you will be studying in Unit 13. As you complete the exercises in this Unit, it may help to refer to the way the words are used below.

Steven P. Jobs: 1955–2011

<Obituary>

Steven P. Jobs

October 6, 2011
By Tomiko Sato

Steven P. Jobs, the charismatic co-founder of the computer company Apple, Inc., died on Wednesday at the age of 56. The cause of death was complications from pancreatic cancer.

The **enormity** of Mr. Jobs's impact on the many industries he touched still remains to be measured. Over the past thirty-five years, virtually since the beginning of his adult life, he grew into an iconic figure that symbolized both the computer revolution and everyday life in the digital age. In the entrepreneurial Mr. Jobs, a mastery of technology **dovetailed** almost seamlessly with a passion for stylish, sleek design and an intuitive business sense. To many consumers, the combination proved irresistible, as the loyalty of millions of Apple customers must **attest**.

Steven Paul Jobs was born the son of a young unwed couple in San Francisco, California, on February 24, 1955. Paul and Clara Jobs adopted the boy and raised him in Cupertino, in what is now known as Silicon Valley. The region was shortly to become the world center of computer technology.

The young Steve Jobs grew up with a pronounced rebellious streak, together with a fondness for mischievous pranks— evidence of a **wry** sense of humor. Youth proved no **impediment** to the child's passion for knowledge and electronics, **steadfast** passions that would last a lifetime. In 1969, Steve Jobs befriended Steve Wozniak, who shared his interest in electronic devices. After Jobs dropped out after one semester at Reed College, he and Wozniak joined a computer hobby club together. Soon after, they went into business together. The two started by assembling personal computers in Mr. Jobs's garage. Thus, in 1976, Apple Computer was born. It was a success from the start.

Steve Jobs and Steve Wozniak at the West Coast Computer Fair in 1977

Crowds await the opening of the first Apple store in Germany.

By 1980, at the age of twenty-five, Mr. Jobs's net worth had exceeded $200 million. Yet numerous twists and turns awaited him in his career. In 1985, after bitter disputes with the Apple Board of Directors, Mr. Jobs was exiled from his own company. Some entrepreneurs in his position might have been expected to become **forlorn** and lose hope. But Mr. Jobs never **faltered** in his determination to be a leader in technology. Without **loitering**, he bought a small computer graphics company and transformed it into the highly successful Pixar Animation Studios. When Pixar went public, Mr. Jobs became a billionaire.

The first Macintosh

In 1997, when Apple's directors again became disenchanted with management, they invited Mr. Jobs back to run the company. By this time, his eccentricities were well known. Never one to suffer fools gladly, Mr. Jobs could be withering in his critiques of colleagues and subordinates: His **pithy** appraisals of their efforts were often characterized as **haughty**, even arrogant, but Mr. Jobs swiftly grasped the **imperative** at Apple. He created an alliance with a man he once **vilified**, Bill Gates of Microsoft, although both men had accused each other of **plundering** trade secrets and stealing technical know-how. Gates agreed to invest millions in Apple—with Jobs at the helm. In just a few years, Mr. Jobs triumphed with a series of innovative products that became emblematic of an upscale digital lifestyle. Although these products were expensive, consumers must have believed that you get what you pay for: Each device captured the market, aided by Mr. Jobs's legendary ability to **adapt** product launches into epochal events.

Mr. Jobs is survived by his wife Laurene, his sisters Mona Simpson and Patty Jobs, and four children.

Audio

For iWords and audio passages, snap the code, or go to **vocabularyworkshop.com**.

Definitions

Note the spelling, pronunciation, part(s) of speech, and definition(s) of each of the following words. Then write the appropriate form of the word in the blank spaces in the illustrative sentence(s) following. Finally, study the lists of synonyms and antonyms.

1. adapt
(ə dapt′)

(*v.*) to adjust or change to suit conditions

As anyone who moves to a new home can tell you, it takes time to _____ to new surroundings.

SYNONYMS: regulate, alter, acclimate; ANTONYM: remain unchanged

2. attest
(ə test′)

(*v.*) to bear witness, affirm to be true or genuine

I can _____ to the truth of her story because I, too, saw what happened.

SYNONYMS: witness, verify, confirm, corroborate
ANTONYMS: deny, disprove, refute, rebut

3. dovetail
(dəv′ tāl)

(*v.*) to fit together exactly; to connect so as to form a whole; (*n.*) a carpentry figure resembling a dove's tail

We may be able to _____ our activities with theirs if we all plan ahead.

We examined the fine _____ the carpenter used to construct the antique chest.

SYNONYMS: (*v.*) mesh, jive, harmonize
ANTONYMS: (*v.*) clash, be at odds

4. enormity
(i nôr′ mə tē)

(*n.*) the quality of exceeding all moral bounds; an exceedingly evil act; huge size, immensity

The _____ of the disaster shocked and saddened the nation.

SYNONYMS: heinousness, atrocity, vastness
ANTONYMS: mildness, harmlessness, innocuousness

5. falter
(fôl′ tər)

(*v.*) to hesitate, stumble, lose courage; to speak hesitatingly; to lose drive, weaken, decline

The newscaster's voice _____ as he announced to the nation that the president was dead.

SYNONYM: waver; ANTONYMS: persevere, plug away at

6. foreboding
(fôr bō′ diŋ)

(*n.*) a warning or feeling that something bad will happen; (*adj.*) marked by fear, ominous

As the hurricane neared, residents of towns along the coast were filled with _____.

All through that long and sleepless night, I was troubled by _____ thoughts.

SYNONYMS: (*n.*) presentiment, premonition

7. forlorn
(fôr lôrn′)

(*adj.*) totally abandoned and helpless; sad and lonely; wretched or pitiful; almost hopeless

When my best friend moved to another state halfway across the country, I felt extremely _____.

SYNONYMS: woebegone, forsaken, bereft, pathetic
ANTONYMS: jaunty, buoyant, blithe, chipper

8. haughty
(hô′ tē)

(*adj.*) chillingly proud and scornful

The _____ tone of voice in which you refused my invitation offended me deeply.

SYNONYMS: disdainful, supercilious
ANTONYMS: meek, humble, unassuming, modest

9. impediment
(im ped′ ə mənt)

(*n.*) a physical defect; a hindrance, obstacle

You must not let _____ in your path keep you from pursuing your dreams.

SYNONYMS: obstruction, stumbling block
ANTONYMS: help, advantage, asset, plus

10. imperative
(im per′ ə tiv)

(*adj.*) necessary, urgent; (*n.*) a form of a verb expressing a command; that which is necessary or required

If you step on a rusty nail, it is _____ that you see a doctor as soon as possible.

The writing of a thank-you note to acknowledge a gift or act of kindness is a social _____.

SYNONYMS: (*adj.*) essential, indispensable
ANTONYMS: (*adj.*) nonessential, unnecessary, optional

11. loiter
(loi′ tər)

(*v.*) to linger in an aimless way, hang around, dawdle

Some students always _____ in the school yard long after classes are over for the day.

ANTONYM: hurry along

12. malinger
(mə liŋ′ gər)

(*v.*) to pretend illness to avoid duty or work, lie down on the job

If you _____ too often, no one will believe you when you really do fall ill.

SYNONYMS: goof off, shirk

13. pithy
(pith′ ē)

(*adj.*) short but full of meaning

A good editorial should be _____.

SYNONYMS: terse, short and sweet, meaty, telling
ANTONYMS: wordy, verbose, long-winded, foolish, inane

14. plunder
(plən' dər)

(v.) to rob by force, especially during wartime; to seize wrongfully; (n.) property stolen by force

In the Old West, rustlers _____ ranches and farms for cattle and horses.

Thieves often use a third party called a *fence* to sell jewelry and other _____.

SYNONYMS: (v.) pillage, loot, sack; (n.) spoils, pelf

15. simper
(sim' pər)

(v.) to smile or speak in a silly, forced way; (n.) a silly, forced smile

Strangers may find it easier to _____ about trivial matters than to have a serious conversation.

The camera caught me with a _____ on my face.

SYNONYMS: (v.) snicker, titter, giggle

16. steadfast
(sted' fast)

(adj.) firmly fixed; constant, not moving or changing

I urge you to be _____ in your efforts to achieve your goals in life.

SYNONYMS: loyal, faithful
ANTONYMS: inconstant, fickle, unreliable, vacillating

17. vaunted
(vônt' id)

(adj.) much boasted about in a vain or swaggering way

The rookie's _____ strength was no match for the veteran's skill and experience.

SYNONYMS: trumpeted, heralded
ANTONYMS: downplayed, soft-pedaled, de-emphasized

18. vilify
(vil' ə fī)

(v.) to abuse or belittle unjustly or maliciously

Voters have become thoroughly disgusted with candidates who _____ their rivals' reputations.

SYNONYMS: malign, defame, denigrate, traduce
ANTONYMS: glorify, extol, lionize

19. waif
(wāf)

(n.) a person (usually a child) without a home or friend; a stray person or animal; something that comes along by chance, a stray bit

The spunky _____ who triumphs over many hardships is a popular character in film and fiction.

SYNONYMS: stray, urchin

20. wry
(rī)

(adj.) twisted, turned to one side; cleverly or grimly humorous

Charles Addams was famous for _____ cartoons chronicling the adventures of a ghoulish family.

SYNONYMS: dryly amusing, droll
ANTONYMS: humorless, solemn, straight

Choosing the Right Word

*Select the **boldface** word that better completes each sentence. You might refer to the passage on pages 164–165 to see how most of these words are used in context.*

1. Most people know the story of Cinderella, a poor, mistreated (**waif, impediment**) who marries a prince and lives happily ever after.

2. Your outstanding report card and teacher evaluations (**attest, adapt**) to the fact that when you apply yourself, you can be successful.

3. Many ad campaigns deliberately (**loiter, vaunt**) the superiority of a product over all its competition.

4. The (**foreboding, enormity**) of the construction project will provide hundreds of jobs for people over the next five years.

5. People who migrate from the suburbs to the city often find it difficult to (**adapt, dovetail**) to the noise and crowded conditions.

Versions of Cinderella's tale have been told around the world for hundreds of years.

6. Thinking it no crime to borrow from the past, Elizabethan dramatists often (**vilified, plundered**) ancient writings for suitable plots.

7. In the opening scene of Shakespeare's *Macbeth*, there is a strong sense of (**foreboding, enormity**) that something terrible is going to happen.

8. The police sometimes use laws against (**faltering, loitering**) to prevent the gathering of unruly crowds.

9. No matter how well qualified you may be, an inability to get on well with other people will prove a serious (**imperative, impediment**) in any field of work.

10. Mutual respect and understanding among all racial and ethnic groups remains a(n) (**imperative, waif**) in the life of this nation.

11. The (**pithy, haughty**) advice given by Ben Franklin in *Poor Richard's Almanac* has rarely been equaled for its good common sense.

12. Despite our own exhaustion, we made one final, (**pithy, forlorn**) attempt to save the drowning swimmer, but our efforts were to no avail.

13. Monday morning seems to be a favorite time for the employees to practice the fine art of (**foreboding, malingering**).

14. I believe that it is (**adapt, imperative**) that we protect our lakes, rivers, and wetlands, as they provide us with clean drinking water.

15. "I did what I thought best at the time," the president replied, "and I deeply resent their cowardly attempts to (**vilify, plunder**) my actions."

16. Ample food supplies in the United States (**attest, vilify**) to the abilities of American farmers.

17. For a time, it was fashionable for supermodels to look like (**waifs, loiterers**), but that undernourished look has lost its appeal.

18. To (**simper, falter**) now, at the very threshold of victory, would mean that all our earlier struggles and sacrifices had been in vain.

19. When she learned that she had not been chosen for the job, she made a (**wry, forlorn**) joke, but this did not conceal her deep disappointment.

20. His (**haughty, steadfast**) attitude toward those he considered "beneath him" was a sure sign of lack of breeding and simple good manners.

21. The director told him to smile like a "dashing man about town," but all he could do was (**adapt, simper**) like a confused freshman.

22. Political leaders should feel free to change their minds on specific issues while remaining (**steadfast, wry**) in their support of their principles.

23. Hordes of savage barbarians swept into the province, committing one (**impediment, enormity**) after another on the defenseless population.

24. The temperaments of the partners in the business (**dovetail, attest**) so well that they can work together without the slightest friction or conflict.

25. Dexter, our beagle, looks so (**vilified, forlorn**) when we leave him behind.

Synonyms

*Choose the word from this Unit that is the same or most nearly the same in meaning as the **boldface** word or expression in the phrase. Write that word on the line. Use a dictionary if necessary.*

1. not permitted to **tarry** after dark _____

2. **unwavering** devotion to the struggle for equality _____

3. the **proclaimed** excellence of the new software _____

4. no tolerance for those who **play hooky** _____

5. **ransacked** the enemy's camp _____

6. misinterpreted his **tongue-in-cheek** comments _____

7. distributed warm clothing to the **ragamuffins** _____

8. when complete bed rest is **mandatory** _____

9. told us they had grave **misgivings** _____

10. often **smirks** when embarrassed _____

Antonyms

*Choose the word from this Unit that is most nearly opposite in meaning to the **boldface** word or expression in the phrase. Write that word on the line. Use a dictionary if necessary.*

1. the **socialite** who lived in a mansion _____

2. a **promising** proposal for a business _____

3. **glowering** at the loud customer _____

4. **discounted** the news of a product recall _____

5. **working hard** on the new job _____

Completing the Sentence

From the words in this Unit, choose the one that best completes each of the following sentences. Write the correct word form in the space provided.

1. It is _____ for us to produce automobiles that will give us better gas mileage and cause less pollution.

2. The testimony of all the witnesses _____ neatly, forming a strong case against the accused.

3. I appreciate that when I asked for your opinion, you gave it in a few clear, direct, and _____ sentences.

4. When we missed those early foul shots, I had a(n) _____ that the game was going to be a bad one for our team.

5. The comedian specialized in the kind of _____ humor that gets quiet chuckles from an audience, rather than loud bursts of laughter.

6. The _____ of the crimes the Nazis committed in the concentration camps horrified the world.

7. In every war, many children are separated from their parents and become homeless _____, begging for food and shelter.

8. The quick recovery of so many patients _____ to the skill of the hospital staff.

9. Her _____ manner said more clearly than words that she could never associate as an equal with a "peasant" like me.

10. Through all the shocks and trials of the Civil War, Abraham Lincoln never _____ in his determination to save the Union.

11. Why is it that people tend to _____ in groups in the middle of the sidewalk, blocking the flow of pedestrian traffic?

12. After the official had fallen from power, his policies were ridiculed, his motives questioned, and his character _____.

13. Unless you take steps now to correct your speech _____, it will be a serious hindrance to you throughout your life.

14. Great skill is required to _____ a novel or short story for the screen.

15. When she attempted to order the meal in French, we discovered that her much _____ knowledge of that language made no impression at all on the waiter.

16. When he was caught red-handed in the act of going through my papers, all he did was stand there and _____ foolishly.

17. A fearful young recruit may _____ in an attempt to avoid dangerous duty.

18. They remained my _____ friends, even at a time when it might have been to their advantage to have nothing to do with me.

19. The _____ expressions on the faces of the starving children moved TV audiences to pity and indignation at their plight.

20. During our absence, a hungry bear invaded the campsite and _____ our food supply.

Writing: Words in Action

1. Look back at "Steven P. Jobs: 1955–2011" (pages 164–165). What lessons about applying your talent and creativity can you learn from Steve Jobs? How can he be an inspiration for you? Using details from the passage, write a brief tribute to Steve Jobs addressing these questions. Include at least two details from the passage and three Unit words.

2. Consider how contemporary society would be different without devices such as the personal computer, the smartphone, portable MP3 players, tablets and e-readers, or similar products. In a brief essay, describe some of the ways—both positive and negative—that these high-tech products have had an impact on the way we live today. Support your views with evidence from the reading (refer to pages 164–165) or from your own knowledge or experience. Write at least three paragraphs, and use three or more words from this Unit.

Vocabulary in Context
Literary Text

The following excerpts are from Silas Marner *and* The Mill on the Floss *by George Eliot. Some of the words you have studied in this Unit appear in* **boldface** *type. Complete each statement below the excerpt by circling the letter of the correct answer.*

1. Jem could be found and made to restore the money: Marner did not want to punish him, but only to get back his gold which had gone from him, and left his soul like a **forlorn** traveler on an unknown desert. (*Silas Marner*)

    Someone who is **forlorn** is NOT
    a. exhausted   c. worried
    b. helpless   d. joyful

2. For how was it possible to believe that those large brown protuberant eyes in Silas Marner's pale face really saw nothing very distinctly that was not close to them, and not rather that their dreadful stare could dart cramp, or rickets, or a **wry** mouth at any boy who happened to be in the rear? (*Silas Marner*)

    Something that is **wry** is
    a. sad   c. fearless
    b. mocking   d. tender

3. Not a word was spoken . . . when Maggie, who had been looking straight before her all the while, turned again to walk back, saying, with **haughty** resentment, "There is no need for me to go any farther." (*The Mill on the Floss*)

    A **haughty** manner is
    a. noble   c. arrogant
    b. playful   d. composed

Geraldine Fitzgerald and Frank Lawton played Maggie and Philip in the 1937 film *The Mill on the Floss.*

4. "You understand book keeping?"

    "No," said Tom, rather **falteringly**. "I was in Practice. But Mr. Stelling says I write a good hand, uncle." (*The Mill on the Floss*)

    A person who speaks **falteringly** does so with
    a. hesitation   c. fear
    b. vigor   d. humor

5. Mr. Tulliver threw himself back in his chair; his mind, which had so long been the home of nothing but bitter discontent and **foreboding**, suddenly filled, by the magic of joy, with visions of good fortune. (*The Mill on the Floss*)

    A **foreboding** is a(n)
    a. wish   c. annoyance
    b. pleasure   d. warning

Interactive Quiz

Snap the code, or go to **vocabularyworkshop.com**

*Read the following passage, taking note of the **boldface** words and their contexts. These words are among those you will be studying in Unit 14. As you complete the exercises in this Unit, it may help to refer to the way the words are used below.*

Now Arriving on Track 1: New York Dry Goods

<Letter>

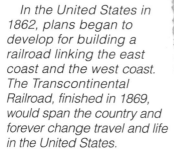

In the United States in 1862, plans began to develop for building a railroad linking the east coast and the west coast. The Transcontinental Railroad, finished in 1869, would span the country and forever change travel and life in the United States.

The last spike of the Transcontinental Railroad is driven at Promontory, Utah, on May 10, 1869.

September 12, 1869

Dear William:

I was pleased to receive your letter inquiring about our operations here in San Francisco. Business has flourished since I opened our western office over a decade ago. The frenzy of the gold rush days has subsided, but there is now sufficient population and enterprise in our region to support a growing commerce. There is steady demand for the dry goods I import from your father's New York warehouse. From time to time, our business is **amplified** by new railroad construction, a new discovery of silver, or a new mine.

I agree with your assessment of our prospects. The completion of the Pacific Railroad, at last linking the coasts of our great nation, marks a new **epoch** in commerce. Yet it would be **naive** to depend entirely on rail transport for our imports anytime soon, or to expect the oceanic traffic to be **obliterated**. Already, the steamers have lowered their prices. Of course, where time is of the essence, we will prefer the overland route. I am **gratified** to report that our first shipments arrived at the new Alameda station. This transcontinental railroad is a sign of progress to come and of a seemingly **infinite** potential in this country. It will drive the growth of commerce. But it is also a measure of what has already been achieved. Would the great men who invested their wealth in this project have **estranged** themselves from their capital if there were not already a great demand for transport across the continent?

As to your prospects, there is always a place for you here, should you decide to come to California and add your strength to the pursuit of our **kindred** interests. The work in our office is for the most part quite **tedious**, though you're welcome to a share if your tastes run to the **bland**. You may prefer to manage shipments to the **vendors** and merchants we supply in California, Utah, and Nevada. I confess I've grown tired of dealings with customers. Too many of them prove **arrogant** and **irascible**. I just overheard a local man arguing with our shopkeeper over the price of some fine linen. The way he put on airs, even pretending the cloth was defective, calls to mind the old saying, the bigger the hat, the smaller the farm. I'd be relieved to put the storefront's oversight in your hands. If you have some other role in mind, we can find a **niche** that suits you.

Recently, I spoke with William Ralston. He had a hand in establishing the Bank of California some five years ago. He is keen to see San Francisco blossom into a great city and says that recent growth in local manufacturing will continue. The city itself, hardly more than a clutter of canvass tents and **ramshackle** houses when I arrived, has matured into a fine urban center. There are many elegant homes, and entertainments enough to keep a young man like yourself occupied in your leisure hours. This year saw the opening of the California Theater, another of Mr. Ralston's projects, which makes an impressive addition to our city life.

I await word of your decision.

Affectionately,
Uncle Albert

For iWords and audio passages, snap the code, or go to **vocabularyworkshop.com**.

Steamer Day, San Francisco, California, 1866

Definitions

Note the spelling, pronunciation, part(s) of speech, and definition(s) of each of the following words. Then write the appropriate form of the word in the blank spaces in the illustrative sentence(s) following. Finally, study the lists of synonyms and antonyms.

1. amplify
(am′ plə fī)

(*v.*) to make stronger, larger, greater, louder, or the like

Some court rulings _____ the authority of the individual states.

SYNONYMS: increase, augment, fill out, supplement
ANTONYMS: lessen, diminish, abbreviate, shorten

2. armistice
(är′ mə stis)

(*n.*) a temporary peace, halt in fighting

Diplomats hope to negotiate an _____ between the warring nations.

SYNONYM: cease-fire

3. arrogant
(ar′ ə gənt)

(*adj.*) haughty, too convinced of one's own importance

An _____ individual is likely to find it difficult to work as part of a team.

SYNONYMS: high-handed, overbearing, presumptuous
ANTONYMS: meek, humble, modest, unassuming

4. bland
(bland)

(*adj.*) gentle, soothing, mild; lacking interest or taste

Some people prefer to live in a place where the climate is _____ and unchanging all year round.

SYNONYMS: dull, insipid
ANTONYMS: harsh, irritating, pungent, spicy, piquant

5. disclaim
(dis klām′)

(*v.*) to deny interest in or connection with; to give up all claim to

Both candidates _____ any ties to special-interest groups.

SYNONYMS: disavow, repudiate
ANTONYMS: admit, avow, confess

6. epoch
(ep′ ək)

(*n.*) a distinct period of time, age

The mapping of the human genetic code marked the start of a promising new _____ in medicine.

7. estrange
(e strānj′)

(*v.*) to drift apart or become unfriendly; to cause such a separation; to remove or keep at a distance

A long and bitter feud may _____ a family that was once close-knit.

SYNONYMS: part company, alienate
ANTONYMS: bring together, reunite, reconcile

8. gratify
(grat' ə fī)

(*v.*) to please, satisfy; to indulge or humor

Experts advise parents not to _____ a child's every whim.

SYNONYM: delight
ANTONYMS: disappoint, dissatisfy, frustrate, thwart

9. infinite
(in' fə nit)

(*adj.*) exceedingly great, inexhaustible, without limit, endless; (*n.*, preceded by *the*) an incalculable number, the concept of infinity; (cap. *I*) a name for God

It may take _____ patience to be a parent, but the rewards are equally great.

A belief in the _____ is a source of comfort and hope to many people who are in distress.

SYNONYMS: (*adj.*) unlimited, boundless
ANTONYMS: (*adj.*) limited, restricted, measurable

10. irascible
(ir as' ə bəl)

(*adj.*) easily made angry, hot-tempered

Working for an _____ boss can be very difficult indeed.

SYNONYMS: irritable, quarrelsome, cantankerous
ANTONYM: even-tempered

11. kindred
(kin' drəd)

(*n.*) a person's relatives; a family relationship; (*adj.*) related by blood; like, similar

If you have any long-lost _____, you may be able to use the Internet to locate them.

People who feel that they are _____ spirits usually have many interests in common.

SYNONYMS: (*n.*) kin, relations
ANTONYMS: (*adj.*) unlike, dissimilar, contrasting

12. naive
(nä ēv')

(*adj.*) innocent, unsophisticated, showing lack of worldly knowledge and experience

A _____ person may be easily taken in by get-rich-quick schemes.

SYNONYMS: green, wet behind the ears
ANTONYMS: sophisticated, knowing, urbane, suave, blasé

13. niche
(nich)

(*n.*) a decorative recess in a wall; a suitable place or position for a person or thing

That _____ in the hallway is a perfect spot for a vase of fresh flowers.

SYNONYMS: nook, alcove

14. obliterate
(ə blit' ə rāt)

(v.) to blot out completely, destroy utterly

An earthquake can _____ large portions of a major city in a matter of minutes.

SYNONYMS: wipe out, erase, efface
ANTONYMS: foster, promote, create

15. ramshackle
(ram' shak əl)

(adj.) appearing ready to collapse, loose and shaky

A few _____ buildings are all that remain of the old mining town.

SYNONYMS: rickety, unsteady, run-down, dilapidated
ANTONYMS: well built, well maintained, shipshape, trim

16. ransack
(ran' sak)

(v.) to search or examine thoroughly; to rob, plunder

Robbers _____ the house for cash and other valuables.

SYNONYMS: rummage, scour; ANTONYM: spot-check

17. rote
(rōt)

(n.) unthinking routine or repetition, a fixed or mechanical way of doing something; (adj.) based on a mechanical routine

Most people learn to type by _____.

_____ memorization can be helpful when you begin to study a foreign language.

18. solvent
(säl' vənt)

(adj.) able to meet one's financial obligations; having the power to dissolve other substances; (n.) a liquid used to dissolve other substances; something that solves, explains, eliminates, or softens

If you want to remain _____, set a budget and stick to it.

To remove tar and paint from your hands, you may have to use a _____.

SYNONYMS: financially sound, in the black
ANTONYMS: bankrupt, in the red

19. tedious
(tē' dē əs)

(adj.) long and tiresome

Sometimes I find it hard to pay close attention to a _____ lecture.

SYNONYMS: boring, monotonous
ANTONYMS: stimulating, interesting, short and sweet

20. vendor
(ven' dər)

(n.) a person who sells something

If the appliance you purchased turns out to be defective, you should return it to the _____.

SYNONYMS: peddler, hawker, dealer
ANTONYMS: buyer, purchaser, customer

Choosing the Right Word

Select the **boldface** word that better completes each sentence. You might refer to the passage on pages 174–175 to see how most of these words are used in context.

1. Every week she meets with a small circle of (**naive, kindred**) souls whose greatest interest in life is the music of Johann Sebastian Bach.

2. Rioters smashed windows and (**disclaimed, ransacked**) government offices as they attempted to overthrow the dictator.

3. A person who behaves with (**kindred, arrogant**) disregard for the feelings of others is likely to have very few friends.

4. He found a comfortable (**niche, rote**) for himself at a bank and worked there quite happily for more than forty years.

5. Although I was furious, I faced my accusers with a (**tedious, bland**) smile.

The music of Bach (1685–1750), a Baroque period composer, has stood the test of time.

6. We are now learning the hard way that our energy sources are not (**infinite, ramshackle**) and that we will have to use them carefully.

7. You will learn that nothing is more (**amplifying, gratifying**) than to face a problem squarely, analyze it clearly, and resolve it successfully.

8. The spirit of the new law to protect consumers is not "Let the buyer beware" but, rather, "Let the (**vendor, solvent**) beware."

9. My next-door neighbor is a(n) (**tedious, arrogant**) individual with a remarkable talent for boring me out of my wits.

10. What is important for the children is not a(n) (**infinite, rote**) recital of the poem but an understanding of what the words really mean.

11. Rather than (**disclaim, obliterate**) their religious faiths, many Protestants, Catholics, and Jews left Europe to settle in the New World.

12. I (**ransacked, gratified**) my brain feverishly, but I was unable to find any way out of the difficulty.

13. In Dickens's novel *Oliver Twist*, the protagonist is so (**naive, tedious**) that he does not understand that he is being trained to become a pickpocket.

14. The beginning of commercial television in the 1940s marked a revolutionary (**niche, epoch**) in the history of mass communications.

15. Several (**vendors, epochs**) at the fair were giving away free samples to entice customers to buy their wares.

16. Whenever my supervisor gets into one of his (**bland, irascible**) moods, I know that I'm in for some high drama before the day is out.

17. Some people are worried that sizable asteroids could hit Earth and (**obliterate, ramshackle**) entire cities.

18. They claim to have "buried the hatchet," but I fear they have only declared a temporary (**vendor, armistice**) in their feud.

19. Over the years, the vigorous foreign policy that this country pursued greatly (**amplified, gratified**) our role in world affairs.

20. The excuse that he offered for his absence was so (**solvent, ramshackle**) and improbable that it fell apart as soon as we looked into it.

21. The business had been losing money for years; but thanks to new management, it is once again (**infinite, solvent**).

22. The job of a mediator is to help (**kindred, estranged**) parties find a basis for settling their differences.

23. Can anyone be so (**naive, irascible**) as to believe that all famous people who endorse products on TV actually use those products?

24. I am willing to forgive you, but I don't know if I can ever (**obliterate, estrange**) the memory of your dishonesty from my mind.

25. Cleaning house is not a difficult chore; it's simply (**bland, tedious**).

Synonyms

*Choose the word from this Unit that is the same or most nearly the same in meaning as the **boldface** word or expression in the phrase. Write that word on the line. Use a dictionary if necessary.*

1. unwilling to **isolate** supporters _____

2. a **merchant** with an old-fashioned pushcart _____

3. **disowned** the wayward son _____

4. **expunged** the evidence _____

5. **routine** performance of the task _____

6. found the opera **dull** _____

7. **turned** the apartment **upside down** _____

8. during an **era** of peace and prosperity _____

9. a **fluid** that removes ketchup stains _____

10. agreed to the terms of the **truce** _____

Antonyms

*Choose the word from this Unit that is most nearly opposite in meaning to the **boldface** word or expression in the phrase. Write that word on the line. Use a dictionary if necessary.*

1. **organized** the hotel room   _____

2. **spur-of-the-moment** actions   _____

3. a report that the applicant is **completely broke** _____

4. **acknowledged** her part in the scheme   _____

5. a **conflict** in the Middle East   _____

Completing the Sentence

From the words in this Unit, choose the one that best completes each of the following sentences. Write the correct word form in the space provided.

1. The Declaration of Independence's assertion that "all men are created equal" marked a new _____ in world history.

2. How could you have been so _____ and foolish as to take their compliments seriously?

3. "Unless we learn to control nuclear weapons," the speaker said, "they may _____ the human race."

4. "You should understand the reason for each step in the problem," our math teacher said, "not simply do the steps by _____."

5. We want to download an application that will _____ our sound effects without distorting them.

6. Because I was obeying all traffic regulations at the time the accident occurred, I _____ responsibility for it.

7. Along the walls of the palace, there were _____ in which statues had been placed.

8. Although she had been separated from her family for years, at her hour of need her _____ came to her aid.

9. We did not realize how poor the people in that isolated region were until we saw the _____ huts in which they were living.

10. Optimists believe that the world is ultimately marked by _____ power and goodness.

11. Increasing dissatisfaction with the direction her political party was taking slowly
_____ her from it.

12. When the electric power failed, we _____ the kitchen to find
candles and matches.

13. He used to be a modest, likable fellow, but now that he has inherited some money,
his manner has become exceedingly _____ and offensive.

14. I've been broke for so long that I'm afraid I won't know how to behave when I find
myself _____ again.

15. The tinkling bell of the ice-cream _____ making his way through
the streets is a pleasant sound on a summer evening.

16. Now that a(n) _____ has finally been arranged, the even more
difficult job of making a lasting peace must begin.

17. After eating so much highly spiced food while on vacation, I craved some pleasantly
_____ home cooking.

18. "A dinner that is truly well prepared _____ the eye as well as the
palate," a famous chef once remarked.

19. After four hours of doing the same small task over and over again, I began to find
my new job _____.

20. I think the vivid phrase "having a short fuse" aptly describes my neighbor's
_____ temperament.

Writing: Words in Action

1. Look back at "Now Arriving on Track 1: New York Dry Goods" (pages 174–175). Suppose you are William's friend, and you have decided to head west. You want to persuade William to join you on the trip. Write a letter using at least two details from the passage and three words from the Unit to convince him.

2. Think about how conveniences like e-commerce, priority mail, overnight deliveries, courier services, and other methods of shipping merchandise quickly have affected the exchange of goods in today's world. Then, in an essay, compare and contrast the business practices of today with those of 1869. Support your essay with evidence from the reading (refer to pages 174–175) or from your own knowledge, experience, or observations. Write at least three paragraphs, and use three or more words from this Unit.

Vocabulary in Context

Literary Text

The following excerpts are from Strange Case of Dr. Jekyll and Mr. Hyde *by Robert Louis Stevenson. Some of the words you have studied in this Unit appear in* **boldface** *type. Complete each statement below the excerpt by circling the letter of the correct answer.*

1. "You start a question, and it's like starting a stone. You sit quietly on the top of a hill; and away the stone goes, starting others; and presently some **bland** old bird . . . is knocked on the head in his own back-garden."

    Something that is **bland** is NOT
    a. true
    b. forgettable
    c. plain
    d. exciting

2. "But it is more than ten years since Henry Jekyll became too fanciful for me. He began to go wrong, wrong in mind. . . . Such unscientific balderdash," added the doctor, flushing suddenly purple, "would have **estranged** Damon and Pythias."

    When people are **estranged**, they are
    a. separated
    b. exhausted
    c. confused
    d. eccentric

3. The middle one of the three windows was half-way open; and sitting close beside it, taking the air with an **infinite** sadness of mien, like some disconsolate prisoner, Utterson saw Dr. Jekyll.

    A sadness that is **infinite** is
    a. foreign
    b. inadequate
    c. immeasurable
    d. fleeting

In the 1931 film version of Stevenson's book, Frederic March played both Jekyll and Hyde.

4. For two months, however, I was true to my determination; for two months I led a life of such severity as I had never before attained to, and enjoyed the compensations of an approving conscience. But time began at last to **obliterate** the freshness of my alarm; the praises of conscience began to grow into a thing of course.

    To **obliterate** something is to
    a. evaluate it
    b. spoil it
    c. protect it
    d. eliminate it

5. At this moment, however, the rooms bore every mark of having been recently and hurriedly **ransacked**; clothes lay about the floor, with their pockets inside out; lock-fast drawers stood open; and on the hearth there lay a pile of grey ashes, as though many papers had been burned.

    Something **ransacked** has been
    a. maintained
    b. gone through
    c. handed out
    d. abandoned

Interactive Quiz

Snap the code, or go to **vocabularyworkshop.com**

Read the following passage, taking note of the **boldface** words and their contexts. These words are among those you will be studying in Unit 15. As you complete the exercises in this Unit, it may help to refer to the way the words are used below.

Muckraking Journalist Ida M. Tarbell
<Biographical Sketch>

Ida M. Tarbell, c. 1904

Ida M. Tarbell was a pioneering investigative journalist. Her 1902–1904 magazine serial exposé, "The History of the Standard Oil Company," did much to reform the United States oil industry. It changed the face of journalism and was the **crucial** catalyst for the breakup of the Standard Oil Trust in 1911. Her nineteen-part **opus** painted a scathing portrait of the shady practices of Standard Oil and its founder and president, John D. Rockefeller, America's first billionaire.

That it was a woman who helped bring down an oil empire may have surprised some in an era when women were still regarded as the "weaker sex." But it did not surprise those who knew Ida Tarbell.

While outwardly modest, with the **veneer** of a polite and proper lady, Tarbell **embodied** daring and courage. She had a passion for exposing the truth.

She also claimed an oil-related **heritage**. Tarbell was born in 1857 in Hatch Hollow, Pennsylvania. Her father became an independent oil producer and refiner in the state's oil-rich region. Young Ida watched as he lost his business due to Rockefeller's **mercenary** practices, which involved **reciprocal** agreements between powerful railroad interests and a select group of large oil refiners. These tactics effectively shut out smaller companies.

Tarbell never forgot the **fiasco** that had **befallen** her father. It played a key role in shaping her later career. After high school, she attended Allegheny College (she was the sole female in her freshman class in 1876). She taught science briefly before becoming a writer. She moved to Paris, France, to work on a biography of a French revolutionary, and returned home at the invitation of a publisher who was starting a political and literary magazine.

Tarbell composed acclaimed pieces for the monthly *McClure's Magazine* on Napoleon Bonaparte and Abraham Lincoln. But this was just a dry run. It was her carefully researched and **rational** articles on illicit industrial practices— **garnished** with her trademark spirited insights—that made her famous. And it proclaimed the era of the Progressive and the muckraker (a term made popular by President Theodore Roosevelt to describe how the journalists "dug up the dirt" on those they investigated).

McClure's Magazine was a leading publisher of muckraking articles. John D. Rockefeller was a prime target of Ida M. Tarbell's groundbreaking journalism.

Shrugging off the **strictures** of conventional journalism, Tarbell and her muckraking cohorts dug deep to uncover injustice and corruption. They avoided the moral **abyss** of yellow journalism, which focused on sensationalism rather than truth. Instead, they presented facts to win over converts to the Progressive cause, which fought for political reform, better working conditions, and civil rights. They targeted hazardous conditions in coal mines, issues of child labor, disease-ridden hospitals, filthy and overcrowded slums, fake patent medicines, and more. Their articles **exasperated** politicians, business tycoons, and bigwigs whose illegal or **negligent** practices were investigated. But they thrilled the public. They also galvanized official investigations and prompted legal reforms. Tarbell's celebrated series of articles on Standard Oil were the opening salvo. A 1911 Supreme Court decision dissolved the oil monopoly into numerous smaller companies. Many of these companies are still active today. The work of the muckrakers led to stricter child labor laws and the passage of the Pure Food and Drug Act of 1906. The muckrakers influenced how investigative reporters work to this day.

Ida Tarbell lived to the age of 84, writing almost up to the day she died. She gained an international reputation as a writer, historian, and editor.

Audio

For iWords and audio passages, snap the code, or go to **vocabularyworkshop.com**.

Definitions

Note the spelling, pronunciation, part(s) of speech, and definition(s) of each of the following words. Then write the appropriate form of the word in the blank spaces in the illustrative sentence(s) following. Finally, study the lists of synonyms and antonyms.

1. abyss
(ə bis′)

(*n.*) a deep or bottomless pit

Mountain climbers must take great care lest they slip and fall into an _____.

SYNONYMS: chasm, gorge
ANTONYMS: summit, promontory, pinnacle

2. befall
(bi fôl′)

(*v.*) to happen, occur; to happen to

It is only natural to worry from time to time about the ills that may someday _____ us.

SYNONYM: come to pass

3. crucial
(krü′ shəl)

(*adj.*) of supreme importance, decisive, critical

In many adventure films, the hero always arrives just at the _____ moment.

SYNONYMS: pivotal, vital
ANTONYMS: insignificant, inconsequential

4. dregs
(dregz)

(*n. pl.*) the last remaining part; the part of least worth

The _____ of bitterness are all that remain of our former friendship.

SYNONYMS: grounds, lees, residue, leftovers
ANTONYMS: elite, cream of the crop

5. embody
(em bäd′ ē)

(*v.*) to give form to; to incorporate, include; to personify

The villain in a melodrama _____ cold-blooded ruthlessness.

SYNONYM: encompass

6. exasperate
(eg zas′ pə rāt)

(*v.*) to irritate, annoy, or anger

Small children sometimes _____ adults with endless questions.

SYNONYMS: vex, try one's patience
ANTONYMS: soothe, mollify, please, delight

7. fiasco
(fē as′ kō)

(*n.*) the complete collapse or failure of a project

With the bases loaded, our star pitcher gave up a home run, turning a close game into a _____.

SYNONYMS: disaster, flop, bomb
ANTONYMS: complete success, triumph, hit

8. garnish
(gär′ nish)

(v.) to adorn or decorate, especially food; (n.) an ornament or decoration, especially for food

The chef _____ our salad with colorful edible flowers.

When it comes to mystery novels, I prefer those that have a _____ of wit.

SYNONYMS: (v.) embellish, gussy up

9. heritage
(her′ ə tij)

(n.) an inheritance; a birthright

A rich _____ of human history and creativity is housed in the world's libraries and museums.

SYNONYMS: legacy, descent, pedigree

10. inert
(in ərt′)

(adj.) lifeless, unable to move or act; slow, inactive

In order to keep patients _____ during surgery, doctors use various general anesthetics.

SYNONYMS: sluggish, lethargic
ANTONYMS: vigorous, energetic, volatile

11. mercenary
(mər′ sə ner ē)

(adj.) acting or working for self-gain only; (n.) a hired soldier, a soldier of fortune

A fortune hunter's motives are _____ rather than romantic.

A country that does not have a standing army may need to call upon _____ to fight in its wars.

SYNONYMS: (adj.) grasping, avaricious
ANTONYMS: (adj.) unselfish, disinterested, altruistic

12. negligent
(neg′ lə jənt)

(adj.) marked by carelessness or indifference; failing to do what should be done

A driver who is _____ about obeying traffic regulations may end up causing an accident.

SYNONYMS: careless, neglectful, remiss, derelict
ANTONYMS: careful, attentive, conscientious

13. oblivion
(ə bliv′ ē ən)

(n.) forgetfulness, disregard; a state of being forgotten; an amnesty, general pardon

Down through the ages, poets have described sleep as a kind of _____ that brings relief from woe.

SYNONYMS: obscurity, nothingness
ANTONYMS: fame, renown, celebrity

14. opus
(ō′ pəs)

(*n.*) an impressive piece of work, especially a musical composition or other work of art

Many scholars consider Michelangelo's Sistine Chapel paintings to be his greatest _____.

SYNONYMS: composition, piece, oeuvre

15. pallid
(pal′ id)

(*adj.*) pale, lacking color; weak and lifeless

A long illness may leave a person looking extremely frail and _____.

SYNONYMS: colorless, bloodless, dull
ANTONYMS: ruddy, sanguine, racy, colorful

16. parable
(par′ ə bəl)

(*n.*) a short narrative designed to teach a moral lesson

Sermons are often based on _____ from the New Testament.

SYNONYMS: moral tale, allegory

17. rational
(rash′ ə nəl)

(*adj.*) based on reasoning; able to make use of reason; sensible or reasonable

Calm and _____ analysis should lead you to a solution to most problems.

SYNONYM: logical; ANTONYMS: mad, insane, illogical, absurd

18. reciprocal
(ri sip′ rə kəl)

(*adj.*) shared; involving give-and-take between two persons or things; working in both directions; (*n.*) (*math*) a number that, when multiplied by another number, gives 1

A _____ understanding of each other's likes and dislikes is important in a close friendship.

The fraction $\frac{4}{3}$ is the _____ of the fraction $\frac{3}{4}$.

SYNONYM: (*adj.*) mutual; ANTONYMS: (*adj.*) one-sided, unilateral

19. stricture
(strik′ chər)

(*n.*) a limitation or restriction; a criticism; (*medicine*) a narrowing of a passage in the body

Most religions impose dietary _____ of some sort on their followers.

SYNONYM: restraint; ANTONYMS: compliment, accolade, swelling

20. veneer
(və nēr′)

(*n.*) a thin outer layer; a surface appearance or decoration; (*v.*) to cover with a thin layer

Some people may adopt a thin _____ of friendliness to hide their true feelings toward others.

Furniture makers often _____ sturdy but common wood with a finer, more costly variety.

SYNONYMS: (*n.*) facing, overlay, façade, pretense
ANTONYMS: (*n.*) nucleus, inner core

Choosing the Right Word

*Select the **boldface** word that better completes each sentence. You might refer to the passage on pages 184–185 to see how most of these words are used in context.*

1. My uncle, who was a West Point graduate, (**embodied, garnished**) all the qualities suggested by the phrase "an officer and a gentleman."

2. What a relief to turn from those (**pallid, negligent**) little tales to the lively, vigorous, earthy stories of Mark Twain.

3. Because decent people would have nothing to do with him, he soon began to associate with the (**dregs, fiasco**) of humanity.

4. "The heroism of these brave men and women speaks for itself and needs no (**oblivion, garnishing**)," said the senator.

The United States Military Academy at West Point originally began as a school for military engineers in 1802.

5. Underneath the (**veneer, oblivion**) of her polished manners, we recognized the down-to-earth young woman we had known in earlier years.

6. If our leadership is timid and (**mercenary, inert**), we will never be able to solve the great problems that face us.

7. As he undertook that big job without any sound preparation, all of his ambitious plans ended in a resounding (**stricture, fiasco**).

8. Isn't it tragic that the religious groups fighting each other are separated by a(n) (**parable, abyss**) of misunderstanding?

9. After his crushing defeat in the election, the candidate returned to his hometown and disappeared into (**heritage, oblivion**).

10. I spent months planning the fund-raiser, but it turned out to be a (**garnish, fiasco**): the guest speaker cancelled at the last minute, and the band was two hours late.

11. Experience teaches us that many of the things that seemed so (**crucial, inert**) when we were young are really of no ultimate importance.

12. When the court found that the car company had been (**negligent, rational**)—selling cars with substandard brakes—it was ordered to pay millions in fines.

13. There are times when it is good to let your imagination run free, instead of trying to be strictly (**rational, crucial**).

14. Marion turned (**opus, pallid**) when she received the news that her grandfather had suffered a stroke.

15. A descendant of one of the Founding Fathers of this country, she strove all her life to live up to her distinguished (**abyss, heritage**).

16. If you are (**reciprocal, negligent**) about small sums of money, you may find that you will never have any large sums to worry about.

17. Using the (**dregs, veneer**) in the teacup, the fortune teller gave the young woman a reading about her happiness.

18. The plan of the two schools to exchange members of their faculties proved to be of (**rational, reciprocal**) advantage.

19. Any significant (**dregs, stricture**) of the passages leading to the heart will hinder the normal flow of blood to that organ and cause cardiac arrest.

20. It's hard for people to admit that some of the misfortunes that (**befall, garnish**) them are really their own fault.

21. In this early novel by Dickens, we have an (**abyss, opus**) that gives us a wonderful picture of life in nineteenth-century England.

22. Such familiar stories as "Little Red Riding Hood" are really (**parables, veneers**) that tell a child something about the conditions of human life.

23. Once the war had been won, the victors laid aside their high-minded ideals and became involved in a (**mercenary, pallid**) squabble over the spoils.

24. Her constant chattering while I'm trying to do my vocabulary exercises (**exasperates, embodies**) me more than I can say.

25. The ancient treasure lies at the bottom of an (**abyss, oblivion**) in the Pacific Ocean.

Synonyms

*Choose the word from this Unit that is the same or most nearly the same in meaning as the **boldface** word or expression in the phrase. Write that word on the line. Use a dictionary if necessary.*

1. a thoroughly selfish and **greedy** individual _____

2. the artist's most brilliant **work** _____

3. remained **motionless** for a long time _____

4. a bad habit that truly **maddens** me _____

5. one who **exemplifies** courage and strength _____

6. a **teaching tale** with an important message _____

7. known to have a **sound** mind _____

8. the **sediment** at the bottom of the pond _____

9. a state of **unconsciousness** _____

10. stared at my **ashen** reflection _____

Antonyms

*Choose the word from this Unit that is most nearly opposite in meaning to the **boldface** word or expression in the phrase. Write that word on the line. Use a dictionary if necessary.*

1. looking for a **factual lesson** _____

2. throwing a **lively** party _____

3. **rosy** cheeks and raven hair _____

4. a place frequented by the **upper crust** of society _____ _____

5. total **consciousness** of the situation _____

Completing the Sentence

From the words in this Unit, choose the one that best completes each of the following sentences. Write the correct word form in the space provided.

1. Would you like your new desk finished with a(n) _____ of walnut, maple, or mahogany?

2. Without pretending that he cared about the public welfare, he told us frankly that his interest in the project was purely _____.

3. To our dismay, the running back didn't get to his feet after being tackled but instead lay _____ on the field.

4. The brief code of laws known as the Ten Commandments _____ basic moral values.

5. A number of famous Roman emperors were clearly madmen for whose actions no _____ explanation can possibly be devised.

6. Winston Churchill warned the English people that if they gave in to the Nazis, they would "sink into the _____ of a new Dark Age."

7. Astrologers claim that they can discover what will _____ a person by studying the movements of various heavenly bodies.

8. Nothing _____ me more than neighbors who play loud music outdoors late at night.

9. She was a famous writer in her own day, but her novels and stories have now passed into _____.

10. Many composers don't publish their works in the order in which they are written, so the number given to a particular _____ might not tell much about the date of its composition.

11. The old adage "I'll scratch your back if you'll scratch mine" aptly describes the kind of _____ arrangement he has in mind.

12. During her confinement in a prisoner-of-war camp, she drained the cup of human suffering to the _____.

13. In this third century of our nation's history, let us continue to safeguard our _____ of freedom.

14. Of course she didn't look well after her stay in the hospital, but a few days at the beach took care of that _____ complexion.

15. The ancient story of the Prodigal Son is a(n) _____ that helps people understand problems and situations of present-day life.

16. In no time at all, poor management turned what should have been a surefire success into a costly _____.

17. The judge imposed a heavy fine on the _____ landlord who had failed to provide heat during the cold weather.

18. My mother doesn't think that a plate of food is ready to serve unless she has _____ it with a sprig of parsley or a slice of tomato.

19. In high school, you will make many decisions _____ to your future, but determining what to wear to the prom is not one of them.

20. The administration intends to propose legislation to cut back on customs duties and relax other _____ on foreign trade.

Writing: Words in Action

1. Look back at "Muckraking Journalist Ida M. Tarbell" (pages 184–185). Think about how the determination of just one person was able to dissolve the powerful Standard Oil Trust. Write a brief report describing how investigative journalists such as Ida Tarbell can help to bring about social reform. Use at least two details from the passage and three Unit words.

2. Think about how the media influences people today and shapes their views of the world. Consider the news you are exposed to on the Internet, on television and radio, and in newspapers and magazines. Do you think the news you receive is presented with only objective facts, or do reporters' and producers' biases shape the information? How do you know when facts are being presented from a particular point of view? In a brief essay, state your opinion and support it with evidence from the reading (refer to pages 184–185) or from your own knowledge or experience. Write at least three paragraphs, and use three or more words from this Unit.

Vocabulary in Context

Literary Text

The following excerpts are from The Turn of the Screw *by Henry James. Some of the words you have studied in this Unit appear in* **boldface** *type. Complete each statement below the excerpt by circling the letter of the correct answer.*

1. [It] was a big, ugly, antique, but convenient house, **embodying** a few features of a building still older, half-replaced and half-utilized, in which I had the fancy of our being almost as lost as a handful of passengers in a great drifting ship.

   The act of **embodying** involves
   a. containing
   b. obscuring
   c. offending
   d. pleasing

2. By the time I reached the pool, however, she was close behind me, and I knew that, whatever, to her apprehension, might **befall** me, the exposure of my society struck her as her least danger.

   If something **befalls**, it
   a. sinks
   b. troubles
   c. transpires
   d. satisfies

3. This opportunity came before tea: I secured five minutes with her in the housekeeper's room, where, in the twilight, amid a smell of lately baked bread, but with the place all swept and **garnished**, I found her sitting in pained placidity before the fire.

   Something that has been **garnished** is
   a. emptied
   b. diminished
   c. dreary
   d. beautified

Ingrid Bergman played the governess in the 1959 television adaptation of *The Turn of the Screw.*

4. With the stroke of the loss I was so proud of he uttered the cry of a creature hurled over an **abyss**, and the grasp with which I recovered him might have been that of catching him in his fall.

   An **abyss** is a
   a. valley
   b. chasm
   c. canal
   d. mountain

5. [I]n spite of my tension and of their triumph, I never lost patience with them. Adorable they must in truth have been, I now reflect, that I didn't in these days hate them! Would **exasperation**, however, if relief had longer been postponed, finally have betrayed me? It little matters, for relief arrived.

   Exasperation is NOT
   a. satisfaction
   b. exhaustion
   c. paralysis
   d. annoyance

Interactive Quiz

Snap the code, or go to **vocabularyworkshop.com**

Vocabulary for Comprehension

*Read the following passage in which some of the words you have studied in Units 13–15 appear in **boldface** type. Then answer the questions on page 195.*

This passage discusses what archaeologists have learned from the mummies left behind by the ancient Inca.

(Line)

When most people think of mummies, they probably think of the kings of ancient Egypt, whose pyramid-shaped tombs are filled with
(5) fabulous riches. But the Egyptians were not the only people who mummified their dead. The Inca Empire of Peru, which flourished long before the Spanish arrived in
(10) the Americas, left behind thousands of mummies. Archaeologists have discovered huge underground burial chambers. The mummies within these tombs and the objects buried
(15) with them are proving to be a treasure trove of clues to how the Inca lived.

At its peak, the Inca Empire was the largest native state that has ever
(20) existed in the Western Hemisphere, with a population of more than 10 million. When an Inca ruler died, his body was mummified and placed within a royal tomb, along with food,
(25) drink, weapons, clothing, and mummified "helpers," including **steadfast** servants and animals. For a year after a ruler's death, his mummy was cared for as if it were
(30) still living. At the end of the year, the mummy was entombed in a great burial hall with other royal mummies,

each seated on a throne. The vast wealth amassed by the kings was
(35) placed in the burial hall with them.

In Inca culture, mummies formed a link between the living and the dead. At festival times, **kindred** carried the mummies through the
(40) streets. This practice proved to people that the rulers had actually lived and that their descendants, who owned the mummies, were part of the royal line.

(45) In the 1990s, burial chambers were discovered on a cliff high in a temperate rain forest in the Andes. Other mummies were found preserved in ice at the top of
(50) mountains regarded by the Inca as sacred places. Some of these burial sites are intact. Others have been **ransacked** by thieves seeking to **plunder** gold and precious artifacts
(55) buried with the mummies. Each new discovery is helping scientists to increase their knowledge of these ancient people. The study of these **inert** remains is yielding details of
(60) Inca life before and after the arrival of Europeans in the Western Hemisphere. Slowly but surely, the secrets of the Inca mummies are being revealed.

1. The author's main purpose in this passage is to
   a. persuade readers to visit Peru
   b. entertain readers with Inca myths
   c. narrate the history of the Inca Empire of Peru
   d. give readers information about the Inca mummies
   e. compare and contrast the ancient civilizations of Egypt and Peru

2. From the first paragraph (lines 1–17), you can infer that archaeologists are scientists who study
   a. plants and animals
   b. ancient civilizations
   c. buildings and houses
   d. the meaning of art
   e. contemporary burial customs

3. The meaning of **steadfast** (line 27) is
   a. faithful
   b. polite
   c. elderly
   d. strong
   e. meek

4. **Kindred** (line 38) is best defined as
   a. priests
   b. friends
   c. workers
   d. relatives
   e. strangers

5. Why did the Inca carry mummies through the streets at festival times?
   a. to arouse people's sympathies
   b. to prove that no one ever really dies
   c. to show their love for a dead relative
   d. to display the wealth of the dead person
   e. to prove that they were descendants of royalty

6. **Ransacked** (line 53) means
   a. broken into
   b. visited often
   c. burned down
   d. emptied completely
   e. searched thoroughly

7. The meaning of **plunder** (line 54) is
   a. sell
   b. loot
   c. collect
   d. preserve
   e. uncover

8. **Inert** (line 59) most nearly means
   a. fragile
   b. ancient
   c. lifeless
   d. priceless
   e. scattered

9. What is the purpose of the fourth paragraph (lines 45–64)?
   a. It introduces an entirely new topic.
   b. It restates all the information in the preceding paragraphs.
   c. It challenges archaeologists' theories about the Inca mummies.
   d. It gives new information about the discovery of burial chambers.
   e. It describes the steps in the process of mummifying dead bodies.

10. The tone can best be described as
    a. serious
    b. critical
    c. humorous
    d. sympathetic
    e. argumentative

11. Which generalization would the writer of this passage agree with?
    a. The ancient Inca Empire was weak.
    b. Much can be learned about Inca civilization from its mummies.
    c. Spanish explorers helped create the ancient Inca civilization.
    d. Ancient Egyptian mummies are better preserved than Inca mummies.
    e. The bodies of dead Inca rulers were treated like those of ordinary citizens.

12. The passage concludes with a statement that expresses
    a. resignation
    b. confidence
    c. cynicism
    d. sadness
    e. indifference

Two-Word Completions

Select the pair of words that best completes the meaning of each of the following sentences.

1. Most immigrants in this country have found it necessary to _____ the traditions they brought with them from their home countries, but few have totally abandoned the rich _____ of their ancestors.
   - a. adapt . . . heritage
   - b. vilify . . . impediment
   - c. plunder . . . veneer
   - d. amplify . . . kindred

2. "You don't need to address issues that will clearly have no effect on the outcome of this election," the campaign manager told the candidate. "But it is _____ for you to take a firm stand on those issues that may ultimately prove _____."
   - a. tedious . . . bland
   - b. naive . . . reciprocal
   - c. gratifying . . . pallid
   - d. imperative . . . crucial

3. "I am certainly _____ that most critics gave my play rave reviews," the author remarked. "But I can't help feeling hurt by the _____ of those who panned it."
   - a. vaunted . . . parables
   - b. exasperated . . . disclaimers
   - c. estranged . . . enormities
   - d. gratified . . . strictures

4. Though police officers in my neighborhood are sometimes accused of _____, let me point out that the diligence with which they solve most cases clearly _____ their overall devotion to duty.
   - a. malingering . . . attests to
   - b. inertia . . . obliterates
   - c. negligence . . . disclaims
   - d. steadfastness . . . dovetails with

5. I love to host dinner parties, but I seldom serve _____ food. I like to spice things up. My signature appetizer, Furious Fava Bean Dip, will not completely _____ your taste buds, but it will make your tongue tingle!
   - a. irascible . . . ransack
   - b. pithy . . . plunder
   - c. bland . . . obliterate
   - d. pallid . . . garnish

6. Acquiring a foreign language can be a(n) _____ chore because it involves so much memorization. If a person didn't have to learn everything by _____, the task would be a good deal less time-consuming.
   - a. foreboding . . . epoch
   - b. exasperating . . . niche
   - c. tedious . . . rote
   - d. irascible . . . heritage

7. "Critics claim that my support for human rights has never been anything but halfhearted," the senator remarked. "However, the record shows that I have been _____ in my commitment to this great cause. Indeed, I take great pride in the fact that I have never _____ in my allegiance to it."
   - a. bland . . . malingered
   - b. steadfast . . . faltered
   - c. inert . . . adapted
   - d. negligent . . . loitered

Adages

In the passage about Steven Jobs (see pages 164–165), the author remarks that consumers are willing to pay higher prices for products from Jobs's company because "you get what you pay for." What the writer means is that more expensive products are usually better-made, more reliable, and more durable than cheap products.

Expressions such as "you get what you pay for" are adages. An **adage** is a brief saying that offers a bit of down-to-earth advice. Adages can be insightful, skeptical, or practical. Because adages have been used so often, they strike us as sensible wisdom spoken by our elders. If overused, however, adages can become clichés.

Choosing the Right Adage

Read each sentence. Use context clues to figure out the meaning of each adage in **boldface** *print. Then write the letter of the definition for the adage in the sentence.*

I. Dario doesn't want to go to the musical, but he should **keep an open mind**. He might really like it. _____

2. Amanda wants to throw a big party with clowns, jugglers, and a pony, but I think **less is more**. _____

3. Spending over a thousand dollars to fix the transmission on that used car you just bought is **throwing good money after bad**. _____

4. Now that I have graduated and been offered a job, **the sky's the limit**. _____

5. Although Nadine did not get the lead role, she will next time. **The cream always rises to the top**. _____

6. I volunteered to take on extra hours at work; I **know which side my bread is buttered on**. _____

7. It must be true that **one man's trash is another man's treasure**, because Brent loves the tacky old velvet painting he found in the alley. _____

8. Don't be upset about losing your job. **When one door closes, another opens**. _____

9. Although Chris slept until noon, he still has to mow the yard, wash the car, and vacuum. **He who rises late must trot all day**. _____

10. I'd better change the oil in my car; **small leaks sink ships**. _____

a. Start late, and you have to hurry.

b. The possibilities are endless.

c. Be receptive to new ideas.

d. I know where my best interests lie.

e. Disappointment is often followed by opportunity.

f. Minor problems can have great consequences.

g. Simplicity is preferable

h. Excellence will eventually be noticed.

i. Useless objects may be valued by someone else.

j. Wasting even more money than you initially wasted.

WORD STUDY

Writing with Adages

Find the meaning of each adage. (Use a dictionary if necessary.) Then write a sentence for each adage.

1. Out of sight, out of mind.

_____

2. Live and learn.

_____

3. Bad gains are true losses.

_____

4. Every picture tells a story.

_____

5. Don't wish your life away.

_____

_____

6. Opposites attract.

_____

_____

7. Forgive and forget.

_____

_____

8. Bloom where you're planted.

_____

9. Different strokes for different folks.

_____

10. Count your blessings.

_____

11. Ill weeds grow fast.

_____

12. It is easier to criticize than do better.

_____

Denotation and Connotation

Words have two different types of meaning. **Denotation** is the precise definition of a word, as found in a dictionary. A word's denotation is neutral; it doesn't carry an emotional charge.

Connotation refers to the emotions and associations a word evokes. These less tangible meanings can carry positive or negative emotional charges.

Consider these synonyms for the neutral word *satisfied*.

> *pleased   gratified   complacent   gloating*

Pleased and *gratified* have positive connotations, whereas *complacent* and *gloating* are negative.

> **Think:** A humble person will probably be pleased or gratified to win a competition, while an arrogant person may be complacent or even gloating after winning a coveted award.

Look at these examples of words that are similar in denotation but have different connotations.

NEUTRAL	POSITIVE	NEGATIVE
plain	mild	bland
inexperienced	innocent	naïve
brief	pithy	terse

Words can have different connotations in different contexts. For example, *garnish* has a positive connotation when used in the context of decoration: *We garnished the cupcakes with colorful sprinkles. Garnish* can have a negative connotation, though, when used in the context of communication: *She garnished the story about her vacation trip with exaggerations and lies.* Always keep the context in mind when you're trying to determine a word's connotation.

Shades of Meaning

Write a plus sign (+) in the box if the word has a positive connotation.
Write a minus sign (–) if the word has a negative connotation. Put a zero (0)
if the word is neutral.

1. epoch ☐   **2.** stricture ☐   **3.** heritage ☐   **4.** obliterate ☐

5. rational ☐   **6.** plunder ☐   **7.** forlorn ☐   **8.** gratify ☐

9. fiasco ☐   **10.** tedious ☐   **11.** steadfast ☐   **12.** vendor ☐

13. opus ☐   **14.** wry ☐   **15.** reciprocal ☐   **16.** loiter ☐

Expressing the Connotation

Read each sentence. Select the word in parentheses that better expresses the connotation (positive, negative, or neutral) given at the beginning of the sentence.

neutral
1. Trina wanted a midnight snack, but all she found were the (**leftovers, dregs**) of the previous night's dinner.

positive
2. When the electricity went out for days, we had to (**adapt, endure**) and live without air-conditioning.

negative
3. Although some people consider Andrea to be (**opinionated, irascible**), she is really quite friendly and cooperative.

negative
4. We bought several T-shirts and other souvenirs from (**vendors, hawkers**) at the county fair.

positive
5. I wanted to (**amplify, increase**) the sound in my home theater, so I spared no expense.

negative
6. The blogger wrote a scathing article (**vilifying, criticizing**) anyone who rides a motorcycle.

neutral
7. Sergio thought his (**pithy, brief**) comments made him appear profound.

positive
8. Why is it that we always want people to (**smile, simper**) when they're around babies?

Challenge: Using Connotation

Choose vocabulary words from Units 13–15 to replace the highlighted words in the sentences below. Then explain how the connotation of the replacement word changes the tone of the sentence.

haughty	exasperate	ramshackle
plunder	falter	attest

1. Several witnesses in the trial could **say** _____ that the defendant was indeed the one who had locked them in the vault.

_____

_____

2. I told Cassandra that her **overconfident** _____ attitude was far from charming.

_____

_____

3. After three weeks of singing in rigorous rehearsals, the young performer's voice began to **fail** _____.

_____

_____

Classical Roots

fect, fic, efy, ify—to make

This Latin root appears in **amplify** (page 176), which means "to make bigger, increase." Some other words based on the same root are listed below.

beneficial	clarify	deify	exemplify
certify	defective	edify	personify

From the list of words above, choose the one that corresponds to each of the brief definitions below. Write the word in the blank space in the illustrative sentence below the definition. Use a dictionary if necessary.

1. to guarantee; to declare true or correct (*"make certain"*)

A notary public _____ that documents, such as deeds and contracts, are authentic.

2. to be the embodiment of; to represent the qualities of

In an old-fashioned melodrama, the hero _____ courage and virtue.

3. to be an example of; to show by example

Awards were presented to students whose conduct _____ the principles of good citizenship and service to the community.

4. favorable, helpful, producing good (*"making good"*)

The _____ influence of teachers has helped many young people to realize their full potential.

5. faulty, not perfect, not complete

Manufacturers will often replace _____ products free of charge.

6. to instruct so as to encourage intellectual, moral, or spiritual improvement

A sermon should _____ those who hear it.

7. to make a god of; to worship as a god

The ancient Romans _____ the emperors Julius Caesar and Augustus posthumously.

8. to make clear or easier to understand

A flowchart can be used to _____ the steps in any operation.

Synonyms

Select the two words or expressions that are most nearly the same in meaning.

1. **a.** steadfast **b.** curt **c.** pithy **d.** resolute
2. **a.** obsess **b.** invalidate **c.** assert **d.** annul
3. **a.** inaudible **b.** crucial **c.** pivotal **d.** vaunted
4. **a.** capacious **b.** ample **c.** bountiful **d.** congested
5. **a.** mediate **b.** belittle **c.** minimize **d.** appease
6. **a.** pertinent **b.** rational **c.** relevant **d.** abashed
7. **a.** hover **b.** excise **c.** muster **d.** amass
8. **a.** foreboding **b.** stricture **c.** premonition **d.** ruse
9. **a.** vex **b.** ostracize **c.** exasperate **d.** waver
10. **a.** aloof **b.** prone **c.** apt **d.** predatory
11. **a.** nullify **b.** proclaim **c.** tether **d.** negate
12. **a.** aghast **b.** wanton **c.** willful **d.** exotic
13. **a.** waver **b.** wallow **c.** convey **d.** falter
14. **a.** bolster **b.** plunder **c.** grope **d.** ravage
15. **a.** facetious **b.** overbearing **c.** personable **d.** arrogant

Antonyms

Select the two words that are most nearly opposite in meaning.

16. **a.** elite **b.** vigil **c.** dregs **d.** antics
17. **a.** articulate **b.** incapacitate **c.** rehabilitate **d.** scoff
18. **a.** oblivion **b.** unison **c.** niche **d.** renown
19. **a.** belated **b.** servile **c.** retentive **d.** porous
20. **a.** forlorn **b.** jaunty **c.** gaunt **d.** cryptic
21. **a.** juncture **b.** abyss **c.** proximity **d.** promontory
22. **a.** blasé **b.** dexterous **c.** fervent **d.** kindred
23. **a.** loiter **b.** preclude **c.** entail **d.** comply
24. **a.** sustain **b.** disdain **c.** wrangle **d.** venerate
25. **a.** volatile **b.** menial **c.** oblique **d.** inert

Analogies

Select the item that best completes the comparison.

26. barter is to **money** as
- a. cite is to vision
- b. abdicate is to throne
- c. mime is to words
- d. rehearse is to tools

27. embargo is to **trade** as
- a. roadblock is to traffic
- b. milieu is to era
- c. promotion is to career
- d. blizzard is to snow

28. doctrine is to **religion** as
- a. formula is to philosophy
- b. precept is to medicine
- c. theory is to science
- d. regulation is to occupation

29. pulverize is to **mortar** as
- a. mold is to kiln
- b. grind is to mill
- c. evaporate is to air
- d. blend is to paint

30. forthright is to **directness** as
- a. solicitous is to indifference
- b. prodigal is to thrift
- c. naive is to vitality
- d. genial is to amiability

31. conspirator is to **Intrigue** as
- a. detective is to fiction
- b. candidate is to ambition
- c. loyalist is to rebellion
- d. traitor is to treason

32. injustice is to **rankle** as
- a. grudge is to encroach
- b. sunburn is to infiltrate
- c. tight collar is to chafe
- d. rubble is to oust

33. knight is to **crusade** as
- a. explorer is to discovery
- b. hunter is to safari
- c. scientist is to experiment
- d. detective is to suspect

Two-Word Completions

To complete the sentences, select the best word pair from among the choices given.

34. Though his father had _____ frugal spending habits in him, the young man misspent his first paycheck on _____ purchases.
- a. bestowed . . . bland
- b. attested . . . caustic
- c. instilled . . . frivolous
- d. ferreted . . . solvent

35. The spectators at the lion cage were amused to see the seemingly _____ animal eat in such a(n) _____ manner.
- a. irascible . . . whimsical
- b. unassuming . . . unflagging
- c. voracious . . . gingerly
- d. disarming . . . tedious

36. The young couple could see that the _____ house, while charming, was in _____ need of repair.
- a. ungainly . . . prodigious
- b. plebeian . . . perceptible
- c. indiscriminate . . . plausible
- d. ramshackle . . . dire

37. As a child _____, Mozart basked in public praise and attention from an early age, _____ his talents all around Europe.
- a. turncoat . . . obliterating
- b. laggard . . . tainting
- c. mendicant . . . ruing
- d. prodigy . . . flaunting

Supplying Words in Context

To complete each sentence, select the best word from among the choices given. Not all words in the word bank will be used. You may modify the word form as necessary.

ensue	pallid	shiftless	plaudits
evolve	purge	malinger	abut
ransack	embody	avail	vie
peruse	fend	estrange	ethical
endow	disgruntled	deplore	ornate

38. Before you fill out the job application, you should _____ the instructions carefully.

39. How can the employers expect any one applicant for the job to _____ *all* the qualities they are seeking?

40. Unless he improves his _____ ways, he will not be successful at that job.

41. A riot may _____ if the crowd is not properly controlled.

42. We had to _____ every room in the house in order to find the missing book.

43. The fans were _____ because they were convinced that their team had lost as the result of bad officiating.

staid	finesse	simper	devoid
opus	levity	fallacy	scavenger
decoy	myriad	stoical	parry
adage	waif	vilify	impending
glut	trepidation	audacious	impediment

44. *Adventures of Huckleberry Finn* is doubtless Mark Twain's most famous and most controversial _____.

45. Of all the _____ woes of humankind, is there anything worse than a toothache?

46. The defense attorney prematurely remarked that the lack of solid evidence against her client would make the _____ trial an effortless victory.

47. With my friend serving as a(n) _____ to attract their attention, we managed to get away without their seeing us.

48. In preparation for the big meet, the track team had a big dinner the night before, feasting on a(n) _____ of pasta and bread.

49. The _____ professor refused to keep up with the advancements in his field, and felt that his students' avant-garde papers were outlandish.

 **Word Associations**

*Select the word or expression that best completes the meaning of the sentence or answers the question, with particular reference to the meaning of the word in **boldface** type.*

50. Apparitions would be likely to play an important part in
a. your history book
b. ghost stories
c. a TV news program
d. a math examination

51. The word **teeming** would not be applied to
a. the streets of a busy city
b. a heavy rainfall
c. a jungle
d. an empty room

52. Which of the following might aptly be classified as **wry**?
a. a loaf of bread
b. a sense of humor
c. twinge of conscience
d. a mole

53. A **recluse** usually prefers to be
a. out-of-doors
b. in good company
c. in a position of power
d. alone

54. People who have reached an **accord**
a. play musical instruments
b. are at the last stop of a bus line
c. are in agreement
d. work at similar jobs

55. A **tractable** person is one who
a. can operate a tractor
b. owns a large tract of land
c. is easily influenced by others
d. is unbearably stubborn

56. The **jurisdiction** of a court refers to
a. the kinds of cases it can decide
b. where the court is located
c. the qualifications of the judges
d. the money needed to run the court

57. A **pseudonym** is most likely to be used by
a. someone traveling incognito
b. a waif
c. a police officer
d. a leading citizen of your community

58. To do something without **stinting** is to be
a. careful
b. stingy
c. generous
d. in bad taste

59. Which of the following might be called **tawdry**?
a. a well-managed farm
b. a center for medical research
c. a one-room schoolhouse
d. cheap, loud decorations

60. A **parable** uses a story to
a. trap a liar
b. make arithmetical computations
c. describe an event
d. clarify a moral idea

61. A person who serves as your **proxy** is
a. a servant
b. a medical specialist
c. one who acts in your place
d. a close friend

Choosing the Right Meaning

Read each sentence carefully. Then select the item that best completes the statement below the sentence.

62. After much experimentation, the scientists finally **devised** a method for eliminating hiccups in mice.

In line 1 **devised** most nearly means

a. discarded   **b.** invented   **c.** borrowed   **d.** explained

63. The world-renowned opera singer **basked** in the limelight.

In line 1 **basked** most nearly means

a. reveled   **b.** hid   **c.** flourished   **d.** faded

64. Firefighters spent four days putting out the **calamitous** fire that burned down half the city.

In line 1 **calamitous** most nearly means

a. sudden   **b.** minor   **c.** devastating   **d.** brief

65. It's astonishing how many adults still believe in the **legendary** Loch Ness Monster.

In line 1 **legendary** most nearly means

a. foreign   **b.** mythical   **c.** fascinating   **d.** historical

66. On the first day of school, the teacher told his students that doing their homework was **imperative** for achieving academic success.

In line 2 **imperative** most nearly means

a. essential   **b.** expensive   **c.** terrifying   **d.** burdensome

67. They had such **divergent** points of view that the two coworkers could not agree on how to execute the project.

In line 1 **divergent** most nearly means

a. similar   **b.** interesting   **c.** conventional   **d.** differing

68. Her travel plans went **awry** when all the bus drivers suddenly went on strike.

In line 1 **awry** most nearly means

a. amiss   **b.** slowly   **c.** forward   **d.** smoothly

69. The animal welfare officers inspecting the neglected zoo were dismayed by how the animals **cowered** in their cages.

In line 2 **cowered** most nearly means

a. growled   **b.** slept   **c.** cringed   **d.** roared

70. Even though his manner of speaking is full of **quirks**, he is a great lecturer.

In line 1 **quirks** most nearly means

a. failures   **b.** peculiarities   **c.** ideas   **d.** mistakes

WORD LIST

The following is a list of all the words taught in the Units of this book. The number after each entry indicates the page on which the word is defined.

abashed, 72
abdicate, 148
abut, 100
abyss, 186
accord, 128
acme, 90
adage, 14
adapt, 166
addendum, 62
aghast, 62
allot, 34
aloof, 72
amass, 34
ample, 62
amplify, 176
anguish, 72
annul, 52
antics, 24
apparition, 62
appease, 138
apt, 110
armistice, 176
arrogant, 176
articulate, 72
assert, 62
attest, 166
attire, 100
attribute, 90
audacious, 34
avail, 100
avowed, 24
awry, 110

banter, 24
barter, 128
bask, 72
befall, 186
belated, 138
belittle, 90
bestow, 148
bland, 176
blasé, 52
bludgeon, 110
bolster, 52
bonanza, 14
bountiful, 24

calamitous, 138
capacious, 148
capitulate, 110
caustic, 148
chafe, 110
churlish, 14
citadel, 14
cite, 138
collaborate, 14
comply, 34
congested, 24
conventional, 138
convey, 90
cower, 62
crony, 100
crucial, 186
crusade, 148
cryptic, 100
curt, 128

decoy, 138
decree, 14
deface, 148
defect, 72
defile, 111
delve, 139
deplore, 52
detriment, 24
devise, 128
devoid, 34
dexterous, 128
dire, 111
disarming, 111
disclaim, 176
discordant, 15
disdain, 63
disgruntled, 111
divergent, 100
doctrine, 90
dovetail, 166
dregs, 186
durable, 25

elite, 34
embargo, 149
embody, 186
encroach, 111

endow, 111
engross, 128
enmity, 101
enormity, 166
ensue, 139
entail, 129
enterprising, 25
epitaph, 63
epoch, 176
estrange, 176
ethical, 63
evolve, 15
exasperate, 186
excerpt, 15
excise, 90
exotic, 91

facetious, 63
fallacy, 149
falter, 166
fend, 111
ferret, 129
fervent, 101
fiasco, 186
finesse, 73
flaunt, 73
foreboding, 166
forlorn, 167
forthright, 73
frivolous, 52
frugal, 25

gallantry, 139
garnish, 187
gaunt, 101
genial, 73
gingerly, 25
glut, 25
grapple, 35
gratify, 177
grope, 15

habituate, 129
haggard, 91
haughty, 167
heritage, 187
hover, 15

impart, 139
impediment, 167
impending, 129
imperative, 167
impunity, 112
inaudible, 63
incapacitate, 35
incognito, 25
indiscriminate, 63
inert, 187
infiltrate, 101
infinite, 177
instigate, 35
instill, 73
intrigue, 63
invalidate, 26
irascible, 177

jaunty, 91
jostle, 15
judicious, 139
juncture, 91
jurisdiction, 64

kindred, 177

laggard, 15
legendary, 26
levity, 149
loiter, 167
longevity, 35

maim, 26
malinger, 167
mediate, 139
mendicant, 149
menial, 91
mercenary, 187
mien, 112
milieu, 139
minimize, 26
muster, 52
myriad, 35

naive, 177
nauseate, 149
negate, 149

negligent, 187
niche, 177
nonentity, 53
nullify, 101

oblique, 26
obliterate, 178
oblivion, 187
obsess, 53
opus, 188
ornate, 53
ostracize, 73
oust, 53
outlandish, 140
overbearing, 140

pallid, 188
parable, 188
parry, 91
penal, 112
perceptible, 101
personable, 129
perspective, 35
pert, 140
pertinent, 112
perturb, 35
peruse, 53
pithy, 167
pivotal, 149
plaudits, 16
plausible, 64
plebeian, 64
plummet, 101
plunder, 168

porous, 53
preclude, 16
predatory, 91
predominant, 112
premonition, 74
proclaim, 102
prodigal, 64
prodigious, 36
prodigy, 112
promontory, 53
prone, 54
proximity, 64
proxy, 102
pseudonym, 74
pulverize, 64
purge, 74

qualm, 54
quirk, 140

ramshackle, 178
rankle, 102
ransack, 178
rational, 188
ravage, 92
recipient, 150
reciprocal, 188
recluse, 112
recourse, 54
regale, 140
rehabilitate, 74
relevant, 36
renown, 112
repercussion, 74

residue, 54
resolute, 74
retentive, 74
revert, 16
rote, 178
rubble, 16
rue, 129
ruse, 150

scapegoat, 74
scavenger, 102
scoff, 129
servile, 16
shiftless, 140
simper, 168
skittish, 36
solicitous, 54
solvent, 178
staid, 54
stance, 92
steadfast, 168
stint, 102
stoical, 102
stricture, 188
sustain, 54

taint, 140
tawdry, 92
tedious, 178
teem, 150
tenet, 150
tether, 36
tractable, 150
transition, 130

trepidation, 130
turncoat, 92

unassuming, 92
unflagging, 102
ungainly, 150
unison, 36
upbraid, 130

vaunted, 168
veer, 26
vendor, 178
veneer, 188
venerate, 26
veritable, 130
vex, 130
vie, 36
vigil, 16
vilify, 168
vitality, 130
volatile, 64
voracious, 150

waif, 168
wallow, 92
wanton, 26
waver, 92
whimsical, 130
willful, 36
wrangle, 16
wry, 168

INDEX

Affixes, 8
Analogies, 11
Context Clues, 7
Literary Text, 21, 31, 41, 59, 69, 79, 97, 107, 117, 135, 145, 155, 173, 183, 193
Online Resources, 13, 21, 23, 31, 33, 41, 51, 59, 61, 69, 71, 79, 89, 97, 99, 107, 109, 117, 127, 135, 137, 145, 147, 155, 165, 173, 175, 183, 185, 193
Reading Passages, 12–13, 22–23, 32–33, 50–51, 60–61, 70–71, 88–89, 98–99, 108–109, 126–127, 136–137, 146–147, 164–165, 174–175, 184–185
Vocabulary and Reading, 9
Vocabulary Strategies, 7
Word Structure, 8
Word Study
    Adages, 197
    Classical Roots, 49, 87, 125, 163, 201
    Connotation and Denotation, 47, 48, 85, 86, 123, 124, 161, 162, 199, 200
    Idioms, 45, 83, 159
    Proverbs, 121
    Shades of Meaning, 47, 85, 123, 161, 199